EOC Geometry

STAAR EDITION

Measuring Up®
to the
Geometry
End-of-Course Exam

Just for Texas!

PeoplesEducation.com

Peoples Education
Your partner in student success®

Editorial Development: Words & Numbers

Editorial Staff: Kerri Fajvan, Katy Leclercq, Jana Sweeney, Amy Priddy Wierzbicki

Production Staff: Steven Genzano, Jennifer Tully, Shawn Whitt

Chief Development Officer: Michael Urban

Chief Marketing Officer: Victoria Ameer Kiely

Vice President, Curriculum and Development: Elisa Eiger

Development Services Controller: Jason Grasso

Director, Asset Management: Kristine Liebman

Production: Planman Technologies

Cover Design: Joe Guerrero, Todd Kochakji

Geometry Advisory Panel:

Melissa Sivernell, Student Achievement Data Coach, Lewisville ISD, Colony, TX

Cindy Schimek, Katy ISD, Katy, TX

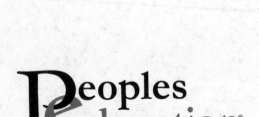

Your partner in student success®

Copyright © 2012
Peoples Education, Inc.
299 Market Street
Saddle Brook, New Jersey 07663

ISBN 978-1-61527-965-4

Manufactured in Newburyport, MA in November 2012 by Bradford & Bigelow, Inc.

Printed in the United States of America.

10   9   8   7   6   5

Table of Contents

Chapter 1   Geometric Structure

Chapter 2   Dimensionality and the Geometry of Location

Note: **Readiness standards are written in bold.** Supporting standards are in plain text.

Chapter 3 Geometric Patterns and Representations

Chapter 4 Congruence and the Geometry of Size

Chapter 5 Similarity and the Geometry of Shape

These full-length Practice Tests were specifically written to match the item formats and testing blueprints for the STAAR Geometry test.

Also available:

Measuring Up Live™

Access our online EOC companion for a multimedia approach—print and online solutions working together for maximum end-of-course support.

Lesson Correlation to the Texas End-of-Course Geometry Essential Knowledge and Skills

This worktext is customized to the *Texas Essential Knowledge and Skills* and will help you prepare for the Texas End-of-Course Geometry test.

Texas Essential Knowledge and Skills	Geometry Lessons
Reporting Category 1: Geometry Structure	
The student will demonstrate an understanding of geometric structure.	
(G.1) **Geometric structure.** The student understands the structure of, and relationships within, an axiomatic system. The student is expected to	
(B) recognize the historical development of geometric systems and know mathematics is developed for a variety of purposes; and **Supporting Standard**	1
(C) compare and contrast the structures and implications of Euclidean and non-Euclidean geometries. **Supporting Standard**	1
(G.2) **Geometric structure.** The student analyzes geometric relationships in order to make and verify conjectures. The student is expected to	
(A) use constructions to explore attributes of geometric figures and to make conjectures about geometric relationships; and **Supporting Standard**	2
(B) make conjectures about angles, lines, polygons, circles, and three-dimensional figures and determine the validity of the conjectures, choosing from a variety of approaches such as coordinate, transformational, or axiomatic. **Readiness Standard**	2, 25
(G.3) **Geometric structure.** The student applies logical reasoning to justify and prove mathematical statements. The student is expected to	
(A) determine the validity of a conditional statement, its converse, inverse, and contrapositive; **Supporting Standard**	3
(B) construct and justify statements about geometric figures and their properties; **Supporting Standard**	3
(C) use logical reasoning to prove statements are true and find counter examples to disprove statements that are false; **Readiness Standard**	4
(D) use inductive reasoning to formulate a conjecture; and **Supporting Standard**	5
(E) use deductive reasoning to prove a statement. **Supporting Standard**	4
Reporting Category 2: Geometric Patterns and Representations	
The student will demonstrate an understanding of geometric patterns and representations.	
(G.4) **Geometric structure.** The student uses a variety of representations to describe geometric relationships and solve problems. The student is expected to	
(A) select an appropriate representation ([concrete,] pictorial, graphical, verbal, or symbolic) in order to solve problems. **Supporting Standard**	3, 5, 12, 18

(G.5) Geometric patterns. The student uses a variety of representations to describe geometric relationships and solve problems. The student is expected to	
(A) use numeric and geometric patterns to develop algebraic expressions representing geometric properties; **Readiness Standard**	5, 12
(B) use numeric and geometric patterns to make generalizations about geometric properties, including properties of polygons, ratios in similar figures and solids, and angle relationships in polygons and circles; **Supporting Standard**	12, 28
(C) use properties of transformations and their compositions to make connections between mathematics and the real world, such as tessellations; and **Supporting Standard**	15
(D) identify and apply patterns from right triangles to solve meaningful problems, including special right triangles (45-45-90 and 30-60-90) and triangles whose sides are Pythagorean triples. **Readiness Standard**	17
Reporting Category 3: Dimensionality and the Geometry of Location	
The student will demonstrate an understanding of dimensionality and the geometry of location.	
(G.6) Dimensionality and the geometry of location. The student analyzes the relationship between three-dimensional geometric figures and related two-dimensional representations and uses these representations to solve problems. The student is expected to	
(A) describe and draw the intersection of a given plane with various three-dimensional geometric figures; **Supporting Standard**	6
(B) use nets to represent and construct three-dimensional geometric figures; and **Supporting Standard**	7
(C) use orthographic and isometric views of three-dimensional geometric figures to represent and construct three-dimensional geometric figures and solve problems. **Supporting Standard**	8
(G.7) Dimensionality and the geometry of location. The student understands that coordinate systems provide convenient and efficient ways of representing geometric figures and uses them accordingly. The student is expected to	
(A) use one- and two-dimensional coordinate systems to represent points, lines, rays, line segments, and figures; **Supporting Standard**	9
(B) use slopes and equations of lines to investigate geometric relationships, including parallel lines, perpendicular lines, and special segments of triangles and other polygons; and **Readiness Standard**	10
(C) [derive and] use formulas involving length, slope, and midpoint. **Readiness Standard**	10, 11
Reporting Category 4: Congruence and the Geometry of Size	
The student will demonstrate an understanding of congruence and the geometry of size.	
(G.8) Congruence and the geometry of size. The student uses tools to determine measurements of geometric figures and extends measurement concepts to find perimeter, area, and volume in problem situations. The student is expected to	

(A) find areas of regular polygons, circles, and composite figures; **Readiness Standard**	18, 19, 20, 21
(B) find areas of sectors and arc lengths of circles using proportional reasoning; **Supporting Standard**	25
(C) [derive,] extend, and use the Pythagorean Theorem; **Readiness Standard**	11, 16
(D) find surface areas and volumes of prisms, pyramids, spheres, cones, cylinders, and composites of these figures in problem situations; **Readiness Standard**	22, 23, 24
(E) use area models to connect geometry to probability and statistics; and **Supporting Standard**	27
(F) use conversions between measurement systems to solve problems in real-world situations. **Supporting Standard**	27
(G.9) Congruence and the geometry of size. The student analyzes properties and describes relationships in geometric figures. The student is expected to	
(A) formulate and test conjectures about the properties of parallel and perpendicular lines based on explorations and [concrete] models; **Supporting Standard**	10
(B) formulate and test conjectures about the properties and attributes of polygons and their component parts based on explorations and [concrete] models; **Supporting Standard**	18, 19
(C) formulate and test conjectures about the properties and attributes of circles and the lines that intersect them based on explorations and [concrete] models; and **Supporting Standard**	26
(D) analyze the characteristics of polyhedra and other three-dimensional figures and their component parts based on explorations and [concrete] models. **Supporting Standard**	22, 23, 24
(G.10) Congruence and the geometry of size. The student applies the concept of congruence to justify properties of figures and solve problems. The student is expected to	
(A) use congruence transformations to make conjectures and justify properties of geometric figures including figures represented on a coordinate plane; and **Supporting Standard**	13, 14
(B) justify and apply triangle congruence relationships. **Readiness Standard**	13
Reporting Category 5: Similarity and the Geometry of Shape	
The student will demonstrate an understanding of similarity and the geometry of shape.	
(G.11) Similarity and the geometry of shape. The student applies the concepts of similarity to justify properties of figures and solve problems. The student is expected to	
(A) use and extend similarity properties and transformations to explore and justify conjectures about geometric figures; **Supporting Standard**	28
(B) use ratios to solve problems involving similar figures; **Supporting Standard**	28
(C) develop, apply, and justify triangle similarity relationships, such as right triangle ratios, trigonometric ratios, and Pythagorean triples using a variety of methods; and **Readiness Standard**	29
(D) describe the effect on perimeter, area, and volume when one or more dimensions of a figure are changed and apply this idea in solving problems. **Readiness Standard**	30

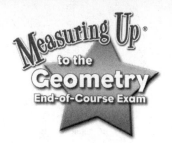

To the Student:

The lessons in this Geometry worktext are geared towards helping you master the TEKS so that you are well prepared for the STAAR End-of-Course exam.

Chapters in this worktext match the STAAR Reporting Categories.

This worktext includes:

- chapters that match the STAAR Reporting Categories,

- a consistent, four-part lesson format,

- end-of-chapter extended-response questions, and

- full-length Practice Tests that were specifically written to match the item formats and testing blueprints for the STAAR Geometry test.

Have a great and successful year!

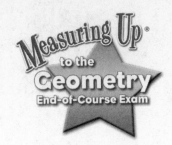

To Parents and Families:

All students need mathematics to succeed. Peoples Education has created this Geometry worktext to help your child master the TEKS so that he or she is well prepared for the STAAR End-of-Course exam, and to get him or her to think on a higher level. As your child moves through this book, encourage your child to consider, analyze, interpret, and evaluate instead of just recalling simple facts.

Each of the 5 chapters in this worktext matches the STAAR Reporting Categories.

This worktext includes:

- chapters that match the STAAR Reporting Categories,

- a consistent, four-part lesson format,

- end-of-chapter extended-response questions, and

- full-length Practice Tests that were specifically written to match the item formats and testing blueprints for the STAAR Geometry test.

For success in school and the real world, your child needs a solid mathematics foundation, and your involvement is crucial to that success. Here are some suggestions:

Show that Geometry is important by including your child in activities that require mathematical thinking.

Help find appropriate Internet sites for Geometry. Note how mathematics is used when you are out with your family. Discuss how mathematics is used in construction and building, in careers such as engineering, architecture, and medicine, in computer programming, and in other real-life situations.

Encourage your child to take time to review and check his or her homework. Just solving a problem is not enough. Ask your child whether the answers are reasonable and have him or her explain what led to that answer.

Get involved! Work with us this year to ensure your child's success. Geometry skills are an essential part of college and career readiness and the real world.

What's Inside: A Lesson Guide

Chapters in this worktext match the STAAR Reporting Categories and Lessons are aligned to STAAR-eligible TEKS.

Guided Practice

Presents you with stepped-out problems and solutions to guide your understanding of geometry skills or concepts.

Additional Problems and Short-Answer Questions

Include short-answer questions that apply the knowledge and skills taught in the lesson.

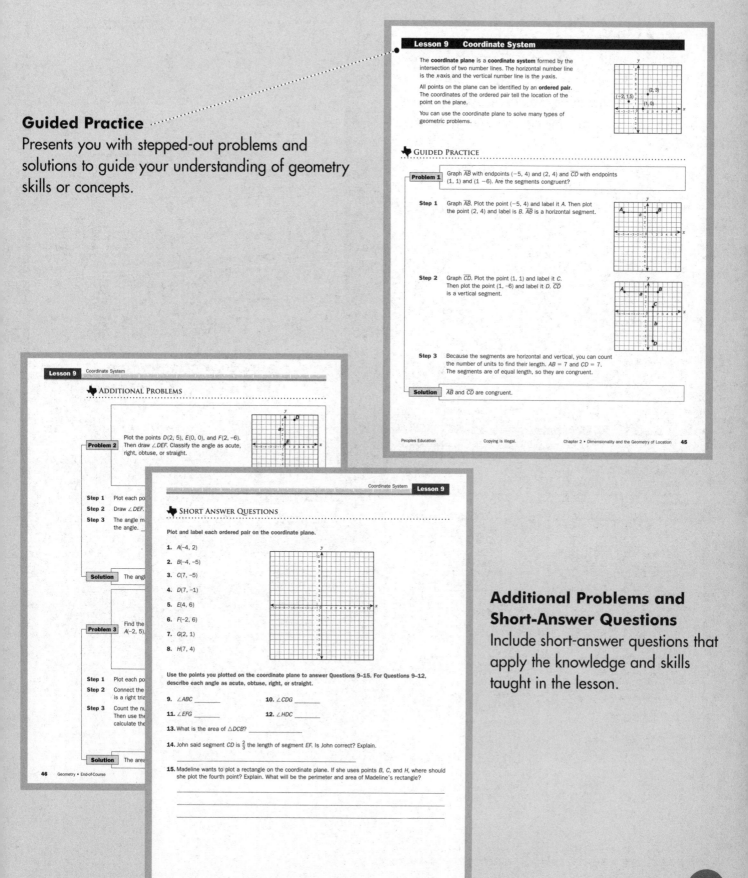

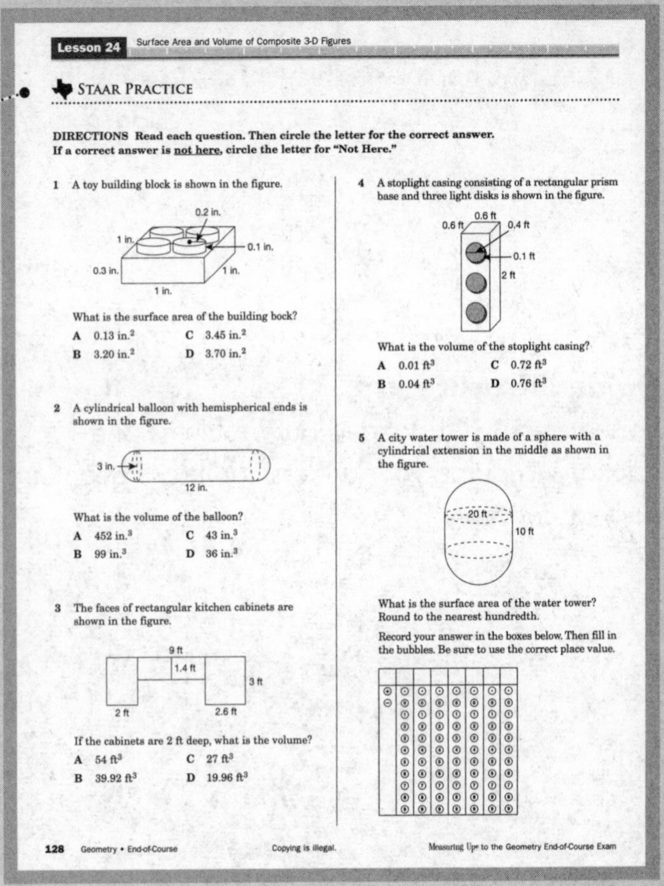
Lesson 24 Surface Area and Volume of Composite 3-D Figures

STAAR PRACTICE

DIRECTIONS Read each question. Then circle the letter for the correct answer. If a correct answer is not here, circle the letter for "Not Here."

1 A toy building block is shown in the figure.

0.2 in.
1 in.
0.1 in.
0.3 in.
1 in.
1 in.

What is the surface area of the building bock?

A 0.13 in.^{2} C 3.45 in.^{2}
B 3.20 in.^{2} D 3.70 in.^{2}

2 A cylindrical balloon with hemispherical ends is shown in the figure.

3 in.
12 in.

What is the volume of the balloon?

A 452 in.^{3} C 43 in.^{3}
B 99 in.^{3} D 36 in.^{3}

3 The faces of rectangular kitchen cabinets are shown in the figure.

9 ft
1.4 ft
3 ft
2 ft
2.6 ft

If the cabinets are 2 ft deep, what is the volume?

A 54 ft^3 C 27 ft^3
B 39.92 ft^3 D 19.96 ft^3

4 A stoplight casing consisting of a rectangular prism base and three light disks is shown in the figure.

0.6 ft
0.6 ft
0.4 ft
0.1 ft
2 ft

What is the volume of the stoplight casing?

A 0.01 ft^3 C 0.72 ft^3
B 0.04 ft^3 D 0.76 ft^3

5 A city water tower is made of a sphere with a cylindrical extension in the middle as shown in the figure.

20 ft
10 ft

What is the surface area of the water tower? Round to the nearest hundredth.

Record your answer in the boxes below. Then fill in the bubbles. Be sure to use the correct place value.

128 Geometry • End-of-Course Copying is illegal. Measuring Up® to the Geometry End-of-Course Exam

STAAR Practice

Includes multiple-choice and gridded items similar to what you may encounter on the STAAR Geometry exam. These items will test how well you understood the skills in the lesson.

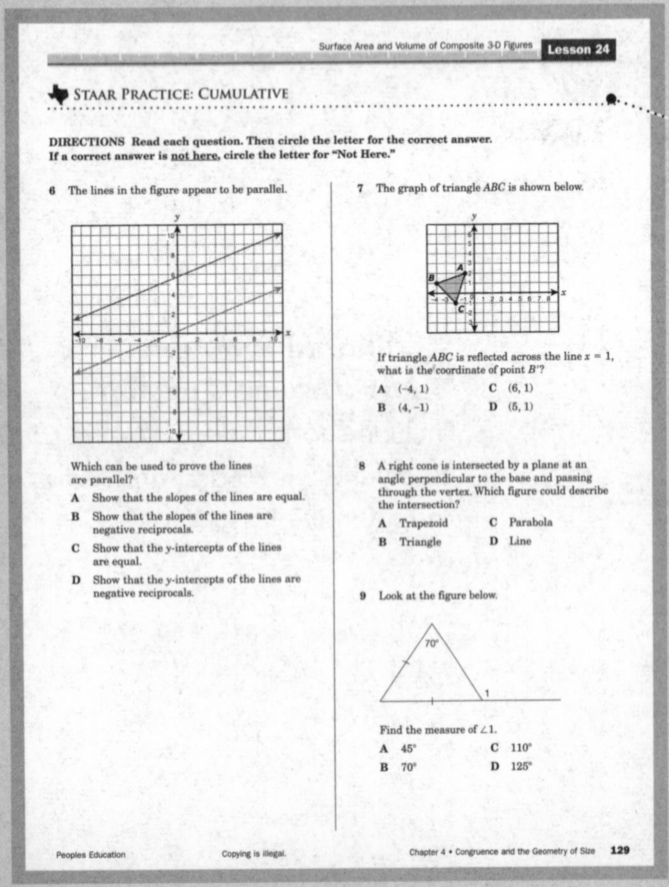
Surface Area and Volume of Composite 3-D Figures Lesson 24

STAAR PRACTICE: CUMULATIVE

DIRECTIONS Read each question. Then circle the letter for the correct answer. If a correct answer is not here, circle the letter for "Not Here."

6 The lines in the figure appear to be parallel.

Which can be used to prove the lines are parallel?

A Show that the slopes of the lines are equal.
B Show that the slopes of the lines are negative reciprocals.
C Show that the y-intercepts of the lines are equal.
D Show that the y-intercepts of the lines are negative reciprocals.

7 The graph of triangle ABC is shown below.

If triangle ABC is reflected across the line $x = 1$, what is the coordinate of point B'?

A (−4, 1) C (6, 1)
B (4, −1) D (5, 1)

8 A right cone is intersected by a plane at an angle perpendicular to the base and passing through the vertex. Which figure could describe the intersection?

A Trapezoid C Parabola
B Triangle D Line

9 Look at the figure below.

70°
1

Find the measure of ∠1.

A 45° C 110°
B 70° D 125°

Peoples Education Copying is illegal. Chapter 4 • Congruence and the Geometry of Size 129

Additional Cumulative Review

Integrates prior lesson skills.

Extended-Response Practice

The extended-response questions at the end of each chapter of this worktext will help you practice answering extended-response questions. These questions require you to write a brief response or explanation based on the text and/or graphics. These questions will also be based on some of the concepts you have reviewed earlier in this book.

A tile pattern consists of square tiles and octagon tiles with an apothem of 3 inches and radius of 3.25 inches.

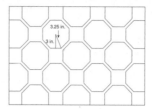

Part A What is the area of one octagonal tile? Show your work.

Part B What is the total area of the tiled rectangle? Show your work.

Part C When laying tile, grout is used between each tile to seal the area between tiles. What is the linear amount of grout, in inches, needed to surround the tiles? (Note: Grout will not be used along the perimeter of the outer rectangle.) Show your work.

Part D A bottle of grout covers 300 linear centimeters. How many bottles will you need to buy in order to grout the rectangular area? Explain your answer.

Lesson 1   Euclidean and Non-Euclidean Geometry

Euclidean geometry is a system based on a set of points in space called a **plane**. A plane is a flat surface that extends infinitely in length and width. A plane has no depth. A line is a set of points that extend infinitely in two opposite directions. A line has length but not width or depth. In the diagram, line *l* lies in plane *P*.

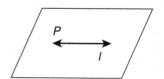

Non-Euclidean geometries define planes, lines, and other geometric shapes differently. Here are some types of non-Euclidean geometry:

- In spherical geometry, a plane is a surface of a sphere. A line in spherical geometry is a great circle. A **great circle** is a circle that lies on the sphere with a center that is the center of the sphere.

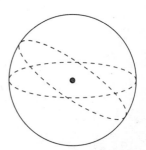

- In taxicab geometry, length or distance is measured along horizontal and vertical line segments. Think of the route a taxicab driver would take in a large city. All movement is horizontal or vertical along city streets. No diagonal or circular movement is allowed.

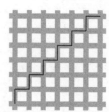

- In hyperbolic geometry, a plane is a curved surface shaped like a saddle.

★ GUIDED PRACTICE

- -

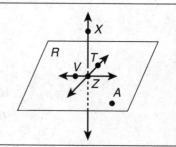

Problem 1   Name all the lines which lie in plane *R*.
Name a point that does not lie in plane *R*.

Step 1   There are three lines shown. $\overleftrightarrow{XZ}$ intersects but does not lie in plane *R*. $\overleftrightarrow{VZ}$ and $\overleftrightarrow{TZ}$ lie in plane *R*.

Step 2   All the points shown except point *X* lie in plane *R*. Point *X* does not lie in plane *R*.

Solution $\overleftrightarrow{VZ}$ and $\overleftrightarrow{TZ}$ lie in plane *R*.
Point *X* does not lie in plane *R*.

✦ ADDITIONAL PROBLEMS

Problem 2 Draw a circle with radius 4 in taxicab geometry.

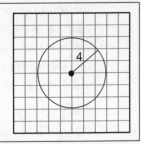

In Euclidean geometry, a circle with radius 4 would look like the circle above. In taxicab geometry, you can only move along horizontal or vertical segments on a grid.

Step 1 Use grid paper. Draw the center of the circle and label it *C*.

Step 2 Move along the possible vertical and horizontal paths that are 4 units from the center. Place a point at the end of each path. You cannot connect the points because the region between them does not lie on a horizontal or vertical segment.

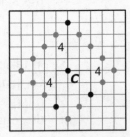

Solution The points of a circle in taxicab geometry form a _____ .

Problem 3 Use the diagrams to describe the sum of the angle measures of a triangle in Euclidean, spherical, and hyperbolic geometries.

Step 1 Describe the sum in Euclidean geometry.

The sum of the measures of the angles of a Euclidean triangle is 180°.

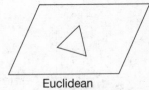

Euclidean

Step 2 Describe the sum in spherical geometry.

The surface of the sphere expands the angles and increases the measures of the angles of a Euclidean triangle. The sum of the measures of the angles of a spherical triangle is greater than 180°.

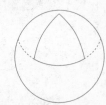

Step 3 Describe the sum in hyperbolic geometry.

The hyperbolic surface contracts the angles and decreases the measures of the angles of a Euclidean triangle. The sum of the measures of the angles of a hyperbolic triangle is less than 180°.

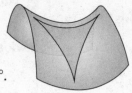

Solution The sum of the measures of the angles of a Euclidean triangle is 180°.

The sum of the measures of the angles of a spherical triangle is greater than 180°.

The sum of the measures of the angles of a hyperbolic triangle is less than 180°.

Measuring Up® to the Geometry End-of-Course Exam

SHORT ANSWER QUESTIONS

Match each system of geometry with its description.

_____ **1.** the study of saddle-shaped space

_____ **2.** the study of flat space

_____ **3.** the study of distance using horizontals and verticals only

_____ **4.** the study of curved space

A	Euclidian geometry
B	hyperbolic geometry
C	spherical geometry
D	taxicab geometry

For each geometric system, tell how many total degrees are in any triangle.

5. Euclidian geometry   **6.** hyperbolic geometry   **7.** spherical geometry

_____   _____   _____

For each geometric system, draw an example of perpendicular lines.

8. Euclidian geometry   **9.** Hyperbolic geometry   **10.** Spherical geometry   **11.** Taxicab geometry

_____   _____   _____   _____

Use the box at the top of the page to answer Questions 12–15. Write the letter of the geometric system used to draw each triangle.

12.   **13.**   **14.**   **15.**

_____   _____   _____   _____

16. Describe a practical application for spherical geometry and hyperbolic geometry.

_____

_____

_____

_____

_____

_____

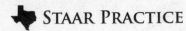

STAAR PRACTICE

DIRECTIONS Read each question. Then circle the letter for the correct answer.
If a correct answer is <u>not here</u>, circle the letter for "Not Here."

1 Which is a true statement in hyperbolic geometry?

  A The sum of the angles of a triangle is less than 180°.

  B The sum of the angles of a triangle is equal to 180°.

  C The sum of the angles of a triangle is greater than 180°.

  D Triangles do not exist in hyperbolic geometry.

2 Which mathematician developed the branch of geometry that studies flat space?

  A Archimedes

  B Euclid

  C Riemann

  D Lobachevsky

3 Which is a true statement in spherical geometry?

  A If t is any line and P is any point not on t, then there exists at least two lines through P that are parallel to t.

  B If t is any line and P is any point not on t, then there exists an infinite number of lines through P that are parallel to t.

  C If t is any line and P is any point not on t, then there are no lines through P that are parallel to t.

  D If t is any line and P is any point not on t, then there is no more than one line through P that is parallel to t.

4 Look at the diagram below.

In which geometric system can the concept of perpendicular lines be represented by the diagram?

  A Euclidian geometry

  B Hyperbolic geometry

  C Spherical geometry

  D Taxicab geometry

5 How many points lie on plane Z?

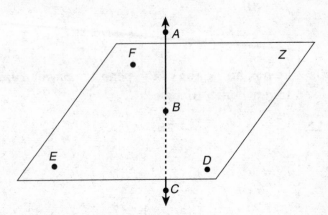

Record your answer and fill in the bubbles on the grid below. Be sure to use the correct place value.

A **conjecture** is a statement made without proof. It is based on knowledge or observation of specific cases. For example, when you find the next number in a pattern, you are making a conjecture based on what you know about the first few numbers in the pattern.

A **geometric construction** is an accurate way of drawing geometric figures and relationships. One way to create a geometric construction is by using only a compass and a straightedge. Another way is by folding paper.

◆ GUIDED PRACTICE

| **Problem 1** | Construct the angle bisector of ∠E. |

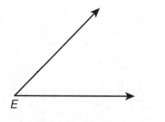

| **Step 1** | Place a compass on the vertex *E* of the angle. |

Draw an arc that intersects both sides of ∠E.

Label the points where the arc intersects the angle *D* and *F*.

| **Step 2** | Place the compass point on *D*. |

Draw an arc in the interior of the angle.

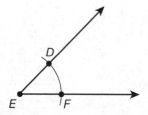

| **Step 3** | Keep the same compass width. |

Place the compass point on *F*.

Draw an arc in the interior of the angle that intersects the arc in Step 2.

Label the point of intersection *G*.

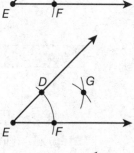

| **Step 4** | Draw $\overrightarrow{EG}$. |

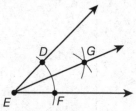

| **Solution** | $\overrightarrow{EG}$ is the bisector of ∠E. |

★ ADDITIONAL PROBLEMS

Problem 2 Use the construction from Problem 1 and a two-column proof to prove $\overrightarrow{EG}$ is the angle bisector of $\angle E$.

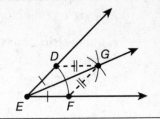

Step 1 Write what is given and what you need to prove.

Given: The angle bisector construction from Problem 1.

Prove: $\overrightarrow{EG}$ is the angle bisector of $\angle E$.

Step 2 Write the two-column proof.

Statement	Reason
1. $\overline{ED} \cong \overline{EF}$	The same compass width was used to create points D and F.
2. $\overline{DG} \cong \overline{FG}$	The same compass width was used from points D and F to form point G.
3. $\overline{EG} \cong \overline{EG}$	_____
4. $\triangle DEG \cong \triangle FEG$	_____ Congruence Postulate
5. $\angle DEG \cong \angle FEG$	CPCTC
6. $\overrightarrow{EG}$ is the angle bisector of $\angle E$.	Definition of _____

Solution You have proven $\overrightarrow{EG}$ is the angle bisector of $\angle E$.

Problem 3 Shamika makes the conjecture that $\triangle ABC$ is an equilateral triangle. Determine whether Shamika's conjecture is valid or invalid.

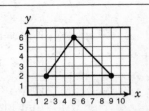

Step 1 Find the coordinates of the vertices of the triangle.

A (_____, _____)   B (_____, _____)   C (_____, _____)

Step 2 Use the Distance Formula to find the lengths of $\overline{AB}$, $\overline{BC}$, and $\overline{CA}$.

$AB = $ _____ $BC = $ _____ $CA = $ _____

Solution The triangle is/is not _____ an equilateral triangle.
Shamika's conjecture is valid/invalid _____.

★ SHORT ANSWER QUESTIONS

Use a compass and straightedge for Questions 1–5. Construct the midpoint of a given segment.

> Given: $\overline{XY}$
>
> Construct: M, the midpoint of $\overline{XY}$

1. Place your compass on point X. Set the compass at an angle greater than $\frac{1}{2}$ XY. Draw arcs above and below $\overline{XY}$.

2. Repeat with Y as the endpoint, using the same compass setting. Label the intersection of the arcs as J and K.

3. Draw $\overleftrightarrow{JK}$.

4. Mark and name the intersection of $\overline{XY}$ and $\overleftrightarrow{JK}$ as point M.

5. Result: _____.

Use your construction above to complete the two-column proof and prove that M is the midpoint of $\overline{XY}$.

Statement	Reason
6. _____	The same compass setting was used to create point J.
7. _____	The same compass setting was used to create point K.
$\overline{JK} \cong \overline{JK}$	**8.** _____
$\triangle XJK \cong \triangle YJK$	**9.** _____ Congruence Postulate
$\angle XJM \cong \angle YJM$	**10.** _____
_____	**11.** _____
$\triangle XJM \cong \triangle YJM$	**12.** _____ Congruence Postulate
13. _____	CPCTC
14. M is the _____.	**15.** Definition of _____.

★ STAAR PRACTICE

DIRECTIONS Read each question. Then circle the letter for the correct answer. If a correct answer is <u>not here</u>, circle the letter for "Not Here."

1 Use the diagram below to answer the question.

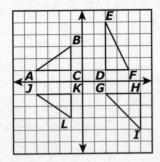

Which of the following is a true statement?

A $\triangle ABC \cong \triangle DEF$

B $\triangle DEF \cong \triangle GHI$

C $\triangle GHI \cong \triangle ABC$

D $\triangle ABC \cong \triangle JLK$

2 Use the construction below to answer the question. Consider the different segments that could be formed using each point.

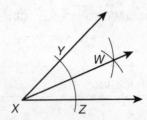

Which of the following is not a true statement?

A $\overrightarrow{XW}$ bisects $\angle X$

B $\overline{XY} \cong \overline{YW}$

C $\triangle XYW \cong \triangle XZW$

D $\overline{WY} \cong \overline{WZ}$

3 Use the diagram below to answer the question.

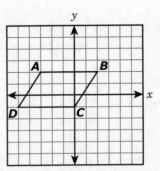

The figure on the coordinate plane appears to be a parallelogram. How could you verify this conjecture?

A Determine the slopes of the sides.

B Determine the length of the sides.

C Determine the lengths of the diagonals.

D Determine the slopes and lengths of the sides.

🟥 STAAR PRACTICE

4   Use the construction below to answer
    the question.

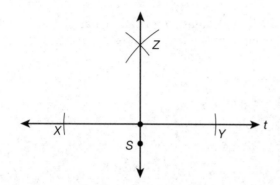

Jodi used a compass and straightedge to make
this construction. Which of the following is a true
statement?

A $\overline{XY} \cong \overline{SZ}$

B $\overline{XY} \parallel \overline{SZ}$

C $\overline{SZ} \perp \overline{XY}$

D $\overline{XS} \cong \overline{SZ}$

5   Use the construction below to answer
    the question.

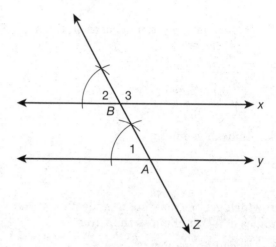

If $m\angle 3 = 120°$, what is $m\angle 1$, in degrees?

Record your answer and fill in the bubbles
on the grid below. Be sure to use the correct
place value.

⊕	⊙	⊙	⊙	⊙	⊙	⊙	⊙
⊖	⓪	⓪	⓪	⓪	⓪	⓪	⓪
	①	①	①	①	①	①	①
	②	②	②	②	②	②	②
	③	③	③	③	③	③	③
	④	④	④	④	④	④	④
	⑤	⑤	⑤	⑤	⑤	⑤	⑤
	⑥	⑥	⑥	⑥	⑥	⑥	⑥
	⑦	⑦	⑦	⑦	⑦	⑦	⑦
	⑧	⑧	⑧	⑧	⑧	⑧	⑧
	⑨	⑨	⑨	⑨	⑨	⑨	⑨

★ STAAR PRACTICE: CUMULATIVE

DIRECTIONS Read each question. Then circle the letter for the correct answer.
If a correct answer is <u>not here</u>, circle the letter for "Not Here."

6 Which geometric system focuses on the study of curved surfaces?

  A   Euclidian geometry

  B   Hyperbolic geometry

  C   Spherical geometry

  D   Taxicab geometry

7 In which geometric system is the sum of the angles of a triangle less than 180°?

  A   Euclidian geometry

  B   Hyperbolic geometry

  C   Spherical geometry

  D   Taxicab geometry

8 Which mathematician is known as the developer of the first comprehensive deductive system?

  A   Einstein

  B   Euclid

  C   Lobachevsky

  D   Riemann

9 In the spherical system of geometry, the shortest distance between any two points is not unique. Which is a real-world example of this concept?

  A   The orbit of the planets around the Sun

  B   The tessellated design for a bathroom floor

  C   The blueprint for a new school gymnasium

  D   The lines of longitude of the Earth

A **conditional statement** has two parts, a hypothesis and a conclusion. The **hypothesis** of the statement is the phrase immediately following the word *if*. The **conclusion** is the phrase immediately following the word *then*. A conditional statement is a logical statement that is either *true* or *false*. Here is an example of a conditional statement.

If **it is raining**, then **I will go to the movies**.

         hypothesis   conclusion

You can use letters and symbols to represent conditional statements. The letter p is used to represent the hypothesis and the letter q is used to represent the conclusion. The symbol "$\rightarrow$" literally means *implies*. So $p \rightarrow q$ is used to represent the conditional statement *if p then q* or *p implies q*. The symbol $\sim$ means *not*, so the statement $\sim p$ means *not p*.

By rearranging and negating the hypothesis and conclusion of a conditional statement, you can create three other forms of related conditional statements.

Type of Statement	Symbolic Representation	Example
conditional	$p \rightarrow q$	If a number is even, then it is divisible by two.
converse	$q \rightarrow p$	If a number is divisible by two, then it is even.
inverse	$\sim p \rightarrow \sim q$	If a number is not even, then it is not divisible by two.
contrapositive	$\sim q \rightarrow \sim p$	If a number is not divisible by two, then it is not even.

To show a statement is true, you must prove it is true for all cases. To show a statement is false you only need to find one case where it is false. A false case is called a **counterexample**.

★ GUIDED PRACTICE

Problem 1

Identify the hypothesis and conclusion of the conditional statement:
If a number is odd, then it is a prime number.

Then determine whether the statement is true or false. If true, explain why. If false, give a counterexample.

Step 1   The hypothesis is the phrase "a number is odd."
The conclusion is the phrase "it is a prime number."

Step 2   The statement is false. The number 9 is odd, but it is not prime.

Solution

The hypothesis is the phrase "a number is odd."
The conclusion is the phrase "it is a prime number."

The statement is false. The number 9 is a counterexample.

🔶 ADDITIONAL PROBLEMS

Problem 2

Write the following statement as a conditional statement.
All right angles have a measure of 90°.

Step 1   Identify the hypothesis and conclusion.
Hypothesis: all right angles
Conclusion: have a measure of 90°

Step 2   Write the conditional statement. You may need to reword the hypothesis and conclusion to do this.

If _____ , then _____ .

Solution

The conditional statement is: If _____ ,
then _____ .

Problem 3

Write the converse, inverse, and contrapositive of the following statement.
Then determine if the conditional statement and its related conditionals are true or false.
If two angles are vertical angles, then the angles are congruent.

Step 1   Identify *p* and *q*, the hypothesis and conclusion.

p: two angles are vertical angles
q: the angles are congruent   The conditional statement is true.

Step 2   Write the converse and determine whether it is true or false. The converse is $q \rightarrow p$.
Converse: If two angles are congruent, then the angles are vertical angles.
The converse is false. Two angles can be congruent without being vertical angles.

Step 3   Write the inverse and determine whether it is true or false. The inverse is $\sim p \rightarrow \sim q$.
Inverse: If _____ ,
then _____ . The converse is false.
Two non-vertical angles can be congruent.

Step 4   Write the contrapositive and determine whether it is true or false.
The contrapositive is $\sim q \rightarrow \sim p$.

Contrapositive: If _____ ,
then _____ .

The contrapositive is true. Two angles that are not congruent cannot be vertical angles.

Solution

The converse "If two angles are congruent, then the angles are vertical
angles" is false. The inverse "If _____ ,
then _____ " is false.

The contrapositive "If _____ ,
then _____ " is true.

★ SHORT ANSWER QUESTIONS

Write the conditionals in if-then form. Then underline the hypothesis and circle the conclusion.

1. The measure of an acute angle is less than 90°.

2. A rectangle with four congruent sides is a square.

3. 3 is a solution of $6x + 2 = 20$.

For each conditional, write the converse. Then determine if the converse statement is true or false. If it is false, give a counterexample.

4. If two angles have a sum of 90°, then they are complementary.

_____

5. If $7x - 1 = 34$, then $x = 5$.

_____

6. If a number is odd, then it is not divisible by 2.

_____

For each conditional, write the inverse. Then determine if the inverse statement is true or false. If it is false, give a counterexample.

7. If an angle is a straight angle, then it has a measure of 180°.

_____

8. If two triangles are congruent, then they have equal perimeters.

_____

_____

For each conditional, write the contrapositive. Then determine if the contrapositive statement is true or false. If it is false, give a counterexample.

9. If two angles are complementary, then each angle is acute.

_____

10. If line a never intersects line b, then the two lines are parallel.

_____

 **STAAR PRACTICE**

DIRECTIONS Read each question. Then circle the letter for the correct answer. If a correct answer is <u>not here</u>, circle the letter for "Not Here."

1 Read the conditional statement.

> Conditional: If two congruent angles form a linear pair, then each angle measures 90°.

What is the contrapositive of the conditional?

A If two congruent angles do not measure 90°, then the angles do not form a linear pair.

B If two congruent angles each measure 90°, then the angles form a linear pair.

C If two congruent angles do not form a linear pair, then each angle does not measure 90°.

D Not Here

2 Which conclusion will form a true conditional statement?

> Conditional: If M is not a midpoint of $\overline{AB}$, then _____ .

A $\overline{AM} \cong \overline{MB}$

B $\overline{AM} \not\cong \overline{MB}$

C $\overline{AM} < \overline{MB}$

D $\overline{AM} > \overline{MB}$

3 Given the conditional statement below, which is true?

> Conditional: If $x = 6$, then $x^2 - 1 = 35$.

A The inverse of the conditional.

B The converse of the conditional.

C The contrapositive of the conditional.

D Not Here

4 Which counterexample proves this conditional statement false?

> Conditional: If two angles are complementary, then the angles are congruent.

A $45 + 45 = 90$

B $90 + 90 = 180$

C $25 + 65 = 90$

D $30 + 30 = 60$

5 Jaime wrote the conditional statement below. Then he wrote the converse, inverse, and contrapositive of his conditional statement. How many of his statements are true?

> Conditional: If the sum of two angles is greater than 90°, then one angle is obtuse.

Record your answer and fill in the bubbles on the grid below. Be sure to use the correct place value.

STAAR PRACTICE: CUMULATIVE

DIRECTIONS Read each question. Then circle the letter for the correct answer. If a correct answer is <u>not here</u>, circle the letter for "Not Here."

6 In which geometric system is a circle represented by a square?

   A Euclidian geometry

   B Hyperbolic geometry

   C Spherical geometry

   D Taxicab geometry

7 Which geometric system is most often used to describe and explore the mathematics of space travel?

   A Euclidian geometry

   B Hyperbolic geometry

   C Spherical geometry

   D Taxicab geometry

8 Use the diagram below to answer the question.

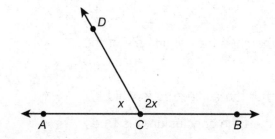

If $\angle ACD$ and $\angle DCB$ are supplementary, which is a true statement?

   A $x = 30°$

   B $x = 60°$

   C $x = 90°$

   D $x = 120°$

9 Use the diagram below to answer the question.

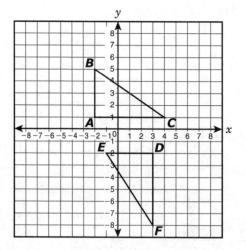

Which statement best describes the relationship between $\triangle ABC$ and $\triangle DEF$?

   A $\triangle ABC$ and $\triangle DEF$ are congruent.

   B $\triangle ABC$ and $\triangle DEF$ are similar.

   C $\triangle ABC$ and $\triangle DEF$ are both similar and congruent.

   D $\triangle ABC$ and $\triangle DEF$ are neither similar nor congruent.

Deductive reasoning uses logic to draw conclusions. It uses facts, definitions, and properties to reach a conclusion.

There are two laws of logic that can help you use deductive reasoning to prove or disprove a statement.

Law of Detachment

If $p \rightarrow q$ is true, and the hypothesis p is true, then the conclusion q is true.

Law of Syllogism

If $p \rightarrow q$ and $q \rightarrow r$ are true statements, then $p \rightarrow r$ is a true statement.

When you write paragraph and two-column proofs, you are using deductive reasoning.

⬥ GUIDED PRACTICE

Problem 1

Use the Law of Detachment to determine whether the conjecture is valid.

Given: If two angles are congruent, then they have the same measure.

     $\angle A \cong \angle B$

Conjecture: $m\angle A = m\angle B$

Step 1   Identify the hypothesis and conclusion of the given statement. The statement is given as true.

Hypothesis: two angles are congruent

Conclusion: they have the same measure

Step 2   You are also given $\angle A \cong \angle B$. This statement matches the hypothesis of the given true statement.

Step 3   Use the Law of Detachment to determine whether the conjecture is valid.

If $p \rightarrow q$ is true, and the hypothesis p is true, then the conclusion q is true.

You are given that $p \rightarrow q$ is true and that $\angle A \cong \angle B$.

The conjecture $m\angle A = m\angle B$ matches the conclusion of the given statement.

You can therefore conclude the conjecture is valid.

Solution   By the Law of Detachment, the conjecture is valid.

★ ADDITIONAL PROBLEMS

Problem 2

Use the Law of Syllogism to draw a valid conclusion from the statements below.

Given: If a figure is a rectangle, then it is a parallelogram.
If a figure is a parallelogram, then it has two pairs of parallel sides.

Step 1 Use the Law of Syllogism. Identify p, q, and r.

If $p \to q$ and $q \to r$ are true statements, then $p \to r$ is a true statement.

p: a figure is a rectangle

q: _____

r: _____

Step 2 Write the conclusion $p \to r$.

If _____ , then _____

Solution

The valid conclusion is if _____ ,

then _____ .

Problem 3

Use a two-column proof to prove that vertical angles have equal measures.

Given: $\angle 1$ and $\angle 2$ are vertical angles.

Prove: $\angle 1 \cong \angle 2$

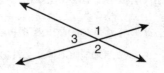

Step 1 List what is given and what you are to prove. Draw two columns. Use facts, properties, definitions, or other postulates and proofs as reasons.

Step 2 Given: $\angle 1$ and $\angle 2$ are vertical angles.

Prove: $m\angle 1 = m\angle 2$

Statement	Reason
1. $\angle 1$ and $\angle 2$ are vertical angles	_____
2. $\angle 1$ and $\angle 3$ form a linear pair. $\angle 2$ and $\angle 3$ form a linear pair.	_____
3. $m\angle 1 + m\angle 3 = 180°$. $m\angle 2 + m\angle 3 = 180°$.	Linear Pair Postulate
4. $m\angle 1 + m\angle 3 = m\angle 2 + m\angle 3$	_____
5. $m\angle 1 = m\angle 2$	_____

Solution

According to the above proof, if two angles are vertical angles, then their measures are equal.

★ SHORT ANSWER QUESTIONS

Match each statement to a law from the box.

1. If $p \to q$ is true, and $q \to r$ is true, then $p \to r$ is true. _____

2. If $p \to q$ is true, and p is true, then q is true. _____

A	Law of Detachment
B	Law of Syllogism

Draw a valid conjecture from the statement(s). Tell which law from the box you used.

3. $\angle A \cong \angle B$ and $\angle B \cong \angle C$. _____

4. If two lines are parallel, then they never intersect. Lines a and b are parallel.

_____

5. If two angles together form a right angle, then they are complementary. If two angles are complementary, then the sum of their measures is 90°. Angles x and y together form a right angle.

_____

6. If a rectangle has four congruent sides, then it is a square. Rectangle *ABCD* has four sides that are 6 cm each.

_____

Tell whether the conjecture is true or false. If false, give a counterexample.

7. Given: If two angles are corresponding angles, then they are congruent. $\angle 4$ and $\angle 5$ are corresponding angles. Conjecture: $\angle 4$ and $\angle 5$ are congruent. _____

8. If a number is an integer, then it is a rational number. If a number is a rational number, then it is a real number. A number x is a real number. Conjecture: x is an integer.

_____

Complete the two-column proof.

Given: $\angle A$ and $\angle B$ are supplementary angles; $m\angle B = 3m\angle A$

Prove: $m\angle A = 45°$ and $m\angle B = 135°$

Statement	Reason
9. $\angle A$ and $\angle B$ are supplementary; $m\angle B = 3m\angle A$	
10. $\angle A + \angle B = 180°$	
11. $\angle A + 3m\angle A = 180°$	
12. $4m\angle A = 180°$	
13. $m\angle A = 45°$	
14. $m\angle A = 3 \times 45 = 135°$	

STAAR PRACTICE

DIRECTIONS Read each question. Then circle the letter for the correct answer. If a correct answer is <u>not here</u>, circle the letter for "Not Here."

1 Use the information in the box below to answer the question.

> If two figures are congruent, then they have the same area. $\triangle ABC \cong \triangle XYZ$
>
> Conjecture: The areas of $\triangle ABC$ and $\triangle XYZ$ are congruent.

Which is a true statement about the conjecture?

A The conjecture is valid by the Law of Detachment.

B The conjecture is valid by the Law of Syllogism.

C The conjecture is valid by the Law of Detachment and the Law of Syllogism.

D The conjecture is not valid.

2 Use the information in the box below to answer the question.

> If two angles are vertical angles, then their measures are congruent. $\angle 1$ and $\angle 3$ are congruent.
>
> Conjecture: $\angle 1$ and $\angle 3$ are vertical angles.

Which is a true statement about the conjecture?

A The conjecture is valid by the Law of Detachment.

B The conjecture is valid by the Law of Syllogism.

C The conjecture is valid by the Law of Detachment and the Law of Syllogism.

D The conjecture is not valid.

3 Kim is using a two-column proof to prove that if $\overline{JK} \cong \overline{MN}$ and $\overline{MN} \cong \overline{PQ}$, then $\overline{JK} \cong \overline{PQ}$.

Statement	Reason
$\overline{JK} \cong \overline{MN}$ and $\overline{MN} \cong \overline{PQ}$	**1.** Given
$JK = MN$ and $MN = PQ$	**2.** Definition of congruent segments
$JK = PQ$	**3.** ?
$\overline{JK} \cong \overline{PQ}$	**4.** Definition of congruent segments

What reason should she write in Step 3 to complete her proof?

A Division property of equality

B Reflexive property of equality

C Substitution property of equality

D Transitive property of equality

4 Which conjecture is true according to the Law of Syllogism?

A Given: If two lines intersect to form a 90° angle, then the lines are perpendicular. Lines A and B form a 90° angle.
Conjecture: Lines A and B are perpendicular.

B Given: If two points are collinear, then they fall on the same straight line. Points J and K are collinear.
Conjecture: Points J and K fall on the same straight line.

C If a triangle is regular, then it is equiangular. If a triangle is equiangular, then each angle measures 60°.
Conjecture: Each angle of a regular triangle measures 60°.

D Given: If two angles are vertical angles, then the angles are congruent. $\angle 1$ and $\angle 3$ are congruent.
Conjecture: $\angle 1$ and $\angle 3$ are vertical angles.

★ STAAR PRACTICE

5 If ∠A and ∠B are complementary angles and
$m\angle A = 2m\angle B$, what is $m\angle A$ in degrees?

Record your answer and fill in the bubbles
on the grid below. Be sure to use the correct
place value.

STAAR PRACTICE: CUMULATIVE

DIRECTIONS Read each question. Then circle the letter for the correct answer.
If a correct answer is <u>not here</u>, circle the letter for "Not Here."

6 Which system of geometry would you use to determine the total walking distance from point A to point B along a grid-based map of city streets?

A Euclidian geometry

B Hyperbolic geometry

C Spherical geometry

D Taxicab geometry

7 Use the figure below to answer the question.

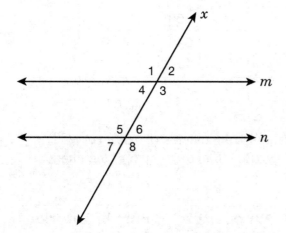

Lines m and n are parallel and line k is a transversal. Which is a true statement?

A $\angle 5 \cong \angle 6$

B $\angle 1 \cong \angle 7$

C $\angle 2$ and $\angle 4$ are a linear pair

D $\angle 7$ and $\angle 3$ are vertical angles

8 Use the conditional statement below to answer the question.

> Conditional: If a quadrilateral is equiangular, then it is a rectangle.

Which is a true statement about the inverse, converse, and contrapositive statements of the conditional?

A The inverse, converse, and contrapositive conditionals are all true.

B Only the inverse and converse conditionals are all true.

C Only the contrapositive conditionals are true.

D The inverse, converse, and contrapositive conditionals are all false.

9 In curved space, as described in spherical geometry, how many straight lines can be drawn?

A 0

B 1

C Infinitely many

D Not Here

A **conjecture** is a statement made without proof.

Inductive reasoning uses examples of specific cases to make a conjecture. Inductive reasoning is not proof. For example, if it has rained every Monday for the last 5 weeks, you could make a conjecture that it will rain next Monday. You also use inductive reasoning when you find the next number or figure in a pattern.

To show a conjecture is true, you must prove it is true for all cases. To show a conjecture is false, you only need to find one case where it is false. This case is called a counterexample.

 ## GUIDED PRACTICE

Problem 1

Use the table and inductive reasoning to make a conjecture about the sum of the interior angles of an *n*-gon.

Polygon Name	Number of Sides	Sum of Interior Angle Measures
Triangle	3	180°
Quadrilateral	4	360°
Pentagon	5	540°
Hexagon	6	720°
n-gon	*n*	?

Step 1   Notice that the sums of the interior angle measures are multiples of 180°. For each polygon, multiply the number of sides minus 2 by 180° to find the sum of the interior angle measures.

Polygon Name	Number of Sides	Number of Sides − 2	Sum of Interior Angle Measures
Triangle	3	1	$1 \times 180° = 180°$
Quadrilateral	4	2	$2 \times 180° = 360°$
Pentagon	5	3	$3 \times 180° = 540°$
Hexagon	6	4	$4 \times 180° = 720°$
n-gon	*n*	*n* − 2	$(n - 2) \times 180°$

Step 2   Make a conjecture.

Solution   The sum of the interior angles of an *n*-gon is $(n - 2) \times 180°$.

⭐ **ADDITIONAL PROBLEMS**
. . . .

Problem 2 | Use inductive reasoning to make a conjecture about the sum of two even numbers.

Step 1   Make a list of the sums of some even numbers.

$2 + 2 = 4$

_____

_____

_____

Step 2   Look for a pattern.
The sums are all _____ numbers.

Step 3   Make a conjecture.
The sum of two even numbers is _____.

Solution | The conjecture is: The sum of two even numbers is _____.

Problem 3 | Cate made the conjecture that for all real numbers $2n > n$. Find a counterexample to show Cate's conjecture is false.

Step 1   List examples.

When $n = 1$, $2n = 2$ and $2 > 1$. The conjecture is true.
When $n = 2$, $2n =$ _____ and _____ . The conjecture is _____.
When $n = 4$, $2n =$ _____ and _____ . The conjecture is _____.

Step 2   The numbers chosen in Step 1 are all whole numbers. You should always try different kinds of numbers when you are looking for a counterexample. In this case, try negative integers.

When $n = -3$, $2n =$ _____ and _____ . The conjecture is _____.

Solution | A counterexample for the conjecture is $n =$ _____.

★ SHORT ANSWER QUESTIONS

Tell whether each statement uses deductive or inductive reasoning.

1. The next number in the pattern 256, 64, 16, 4, 1 is $\frac{1}{4}$.

_____

2. Angles x and y are supplementary by the definition of supplementary.

_____

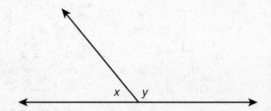

3. The triangles are congruent by SAS.

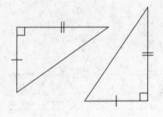

_____

4. The next figure in the pattern will have 25 dots.

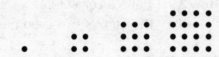

Figure 1   Figure 2   Figure 3   Figure 4

_____

Use inductive reasoning to find the next two numbers in the pattern.

5. 15, 22, 29, 36, 43 _____

6. 45, 15, 5, $\frac{5}{3}$, $\frac{5}{9}$ _____

7. −1, −2, −4, −8, −16 _____

8. 0, 1, 8, 27, 64 _____

For Questions 9–12, use inductive reasoning to make a conjecture.

9. Make a conjecture about the difference of two odd numbers.

_____

10. Make a conjecture about the quotient of two positive rational numbers.

_____

11. Make a conjecture about the angles formed by the intersection of two lines.

_____

12. Make a conjecture about the volume of a series of cubes.

_____

_____

13. Joel made a conjecture that for all integers, $-n < 0$. Find a counterexample to show Joel's conjecture is false.

_____

🔶 STAAR PRACTICE
••

DIRECTIONS Read each question. Then circle the letter for the correct answer.
If a correct answer is <u>not here</u>, circle the letter for "Not Here."

1 Which conjecture is an example of inductive reasoning?

A Two triangles are congruent by the SSA Congruence Postulate.

B Two angles are complementary by the definition of complementary.

C The next figure in a geometric pattern includes 49 dots in a grid pattern.

D Two lines are perpendicular by the theorem that states two lines are perpendicular if they form two pairs of congruent adjacent angles.

2 Using inductive reasoning, Eric wrote the conjecture below.

> Conjecture: For all real numbers, the product of two negative numbers is greater than either factor.

Which is a true statement about Eric's conjecture?

A It is true because the product of two negative numbers is a positive number, and any positive number is greater than a negative number.

B It is true because the product of two real numbers is always greater than either factor.

C It is false because the product of two fractional factors is less than either factor.

D It is false because the product of two negative numbers is a negative number and if the factors are fractions, the product is less than either factor.

3 Which is true about inductive reasoning?

A It uses a two-column proof.

B It uses experimentation and patterns.

C It uses definitions.

D It uses postulates and theorems.

Use inductive reasoning and the pattern below to answer Questions 4 and 5.

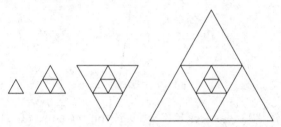

4 Which algebraic expression could you use to determine the nth term in the pattern?

A $n + 3$ **C** $2n - 3$

B $n^2 + 3$ **D** $4n - 3$

5 How many triangles will there be in the next figure in the pattern?

Record your answer and fill in the bubbles on the grid below. Be sure to use the correct place value.

⬥ **STAAR PRACTICE: CUMULATIVE**

. . . .

DIRECTIONS Read each question. Then circle the letter for the correct answer. If a correct answer is <u>not here</u>, circle the letter for "Not Here."

6 Joyce used a compass and straightedge to draw the figure below.

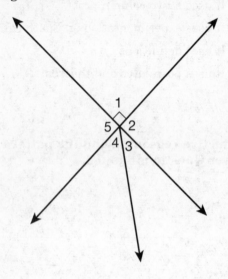

If ∠3 measures 38°, what is the measure of ∠4?

A 38°

B 52°

C 90°

D 142°

7 Use the conditional statement below to answer the question.

> Conditional: If two angles are vertical, then they are congruent.

Which is a true statement?

A The conditional statement is invalid.

B The converse statement is valid.

C The inverse statement is valid.

D The contrapositive statement is valid.

8 Victor made the conjecture that for all real numbers, $2n^2 + 1$ is a prime number. Which is a counterexample that proves Victor's conjecture false?

A $n = 1$

B $n = 2$

C $n = 3$

D $n = 6$

9 Dave used a compass and straightedge to draw the construction below.

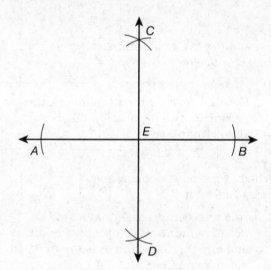

Which reason can Dave write in his two-column proof to justify the statement $\overline{EC} \cong \overline{EC}$?

A Reflexive Property of Congruence

B Substitution Property of Congruence

C Symmetric Property of Congruence

D Transitive Property of Congruence

Measuring Up® to the Geometry End-of-Course Exam

Eli is writing a set of conditional statements about negative integers.

Part A   Write a true conditional statement in *if-then* form concerning the quotient of two negative integers.

Part B   Write the converse, inverse, and contrapositive statements of your conditional statement from Part A.

Part C   Tell whether each statement from Part B is true or false. Give a counterexample for all false statements.

Quinn drew this construction using a compass and straightedge.

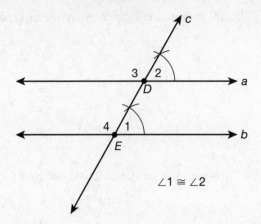

Part A   Quinn makes the conjecture that lines *a* and *b* are parallel. Is Quinn's conjecture valid or invalid? Justify.

Part B   Write a valid conjecture about the relationship of ∠1 and ∠4. Justify the conjecture. Tell whether you used the Law of Detachment or the Law of Syllogism.

Part C   Write a valid conjecture about the relationship of ∠3 and ∠4. Justify the conjecture. Tell whether you used inductive or deductive reasoning.

A **cross section** is the intersection of a solid and a plane.

The figure created by the intersection depends on how the plane intersects the solid. The figures below show three ways a plane can intersect a prism.

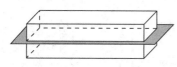 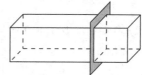 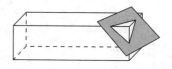

A horizontal cross section is parallel to the base. The figure it creates is a rectangle congruent to the base of the prism.

A vertical cross section is perpendicular to the base. The figure it creates is a rectangle whose dimensions are the width and height of the prism.

This example of an angled cross section slices a corner off of the prism to create a triangle.

 GUIDED PRACTICE

Problem 1 Describe each cross section of the cone.

Cross section 1

Cross section 2

Cross section 3

Step 1 Cross section 1 is a horizontal cross section of a plane and a cone. Because the cross section is parallel to the circular base, it is a circle.

Step 2 Cross section 2 is a vertical cross section of a plane and a cone. The intersection is a triangle. The vertices of the triangle are two points on the base and the third point is the vertex.

Step 3 Cross section 3 is an angled cross section. The plane intersects the curved lateral surface at an angle. The cross section is an ellipse.

Solution Cross section 1 is a circle.
Cross section 2 is a triangle.
Cross diection 3 is an ellipse.

★ ADDITIONAL PROBLEMS

Cross section 1

Problem 2 Describe each cross section of the square pyramid.

Cross section 2

Cross section 3

Step 1 Cross section 1 is a horizontal cross section of a plane and a square pyramid. Because the cross section is parallel to the base, it is a(n) _____.

Step 2 Cross section 2 is an angled cross section. Because the figure is a pyramid, the bottom of the cross section is longer than the top. The cross section is a(n) _____.

Step 3 Cross section 3 is a vertical cross section of a plane and a pyramid. The intersection is a(n) _____.

Solution
Cross section 1 is a(n) _____.
Cross section 2 is a(n) _____.
Cross section 3 is a(n) _____.

Problem 3 A designer wants to create a cross section of the cube that forms a hexagon. She made the slice shown, but it is not a hexagon. What is the shape formed by her cross section slice? How should the slice be made so that the shape forms a hexagon?

Step 1 Determine the shape of the designer's cross section. Her cross section creates a quadrilateral with parallel bases that are not the same length. The cross section is a[n] _____.

Step 2 To form a hexagon, cut through the _____ of the edges.

Solution
The cross section the designer made is a[n] _____.
Cut through the _____ of the edges to form a hexagon.

★ SHORT ANSWER QUESTIONS

Describe each cross-section of the cube.

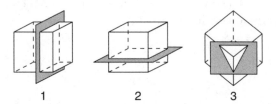

1. _____ 2. _____ 3. _____

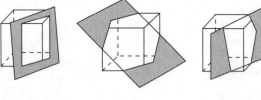

4. _____ 5. _____ 6. _____

Describe the shape of the cross-section formed by the cross-section cut of each figure.

7. horizontal cross-section _____

8. vertical cross-section _____

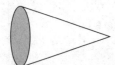

9. horizontal cross-section _____

10. vertical cross-section _____

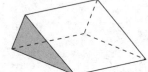

11. horizontal cross-section _____

12. vertical cross-section _____

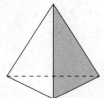

13. Name all the different cross-section shapes that can be formed by cutting cross-sections of a cylinder.

_____

14. How could you cut a cross-section in a cone to form a cross-section that is shaped like a parabola?

_____

_____

⭑ **STAAR PRACTICE**

DIRECTIONS Read each question. Then circle the letter for the correct answer.
If a correct answer is <u>not here</u>, circle the letter for "Not Here."

1 The figure shows a plane intersecting a rectangular pyramid.

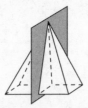

What is the shape of the cross-section?

A Rectangle

B Square

C Triangle

D Not Here

2 The figure shows a plane intersecting a cube.

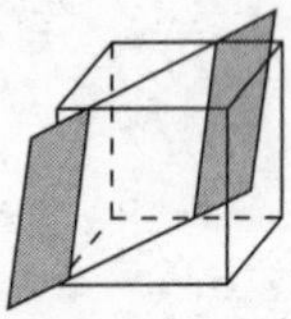

What is the shape of the cross-section?

A Equilateral triangle

B Isosceles triangle

C Parallelogram

D Rectangle

3 Which type of cut will form an elliptical cross-section in a cylinder?

A Cut at an angle

B Cut parallel to the circular base

C Cut perpendicular to the circular base

D Not Here

4 Which cross-section shape could not be formed by the intersection of a plane and a rectangular prism?

A Rectangle

B Octagon

C Square

D Triangle

5 How many different cross-section shapes can be formed by cutting cross-sections of a sphere?

Record your answer and fill in the bubbles on the grid below. Be sure to use the correct place value.

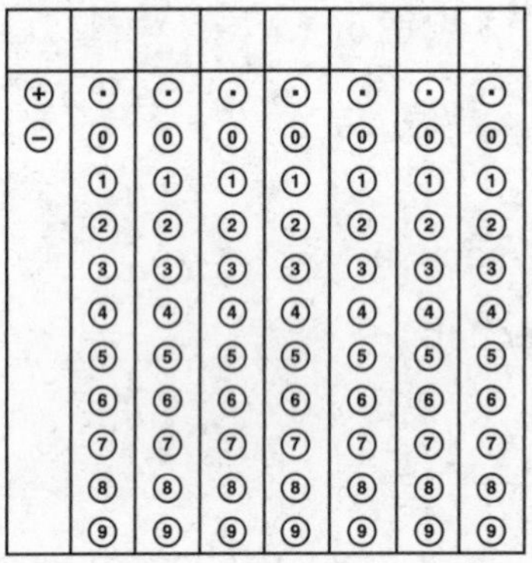

⊕	⊙	⊙	⊙	⊙	⊙	⊙	⊙
⊖	⓪	⓪	⓪	⓪	⓪	⓪	⓪
	①	①	①	①	①	①	①
	②	②	②	②	②	②	②
	③	③	③	③	③	③	③
	④	④	④	④	④	④	④
	⑤	⑤	⑤	⑤	⑤	⑤	⑤
	⑥	⑥	⑥	⑥	⑥	⑥	⑥
	⑦	⑦	⑦	⑦	⑦	⑦	⑦
	⑧	⑧	⑧	⑧	⑧	⑧	⑧
	⑨	⑨	⑨	⑨	⑨	⑨	⑨

Measuring Up® to the Geometry End-of-Course Exam

⭐ STAAR PRACTICE: CUMULATIVE

**DIRECTIONS Read each question. Then circle the letter for the correct answer.
If a correct answer is <u>not here</u>, circle the letter for "Not Here."**

6 Jada constructed the figure below using a
compass and straightedge.

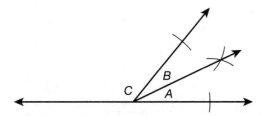

Which is a true statement?

A $m\angle A = m\angle B$

B $m\angle A > m\angle B$

C $m\angle A < m\angle B$

D $m\angle A + m\angle B = m\angle C$

7 Use the pattern below to answer the question.

> 10, 1, 0.1, 0.01, 0.001

Which is the 8th term in the pattern?

A 0.000000001

B 0.00000001

C 0.0000001

D 0.000001

8 Use the information in the box below to answer
the question.

> If two lines are perpendicular, then they
> form a 90° angle at their intersection
> point. Lines c and d are perpendicular.
>
> Conjecture: Lines c and d form a 90° angle
> at their intersection point.

Which is a true statement about the conjecture?

A It is valid by the Law of Syllogism.

B It is valid by the Law of Detachment.

C It is valid by the Law of Detachment and
the Law of Syllogism.

D It is not valid.

9 Kai wrote the following conjecture.

> Conjecture: The sum of a negative integer
> and a positive integer is a negative integer.

Which proves Kai's conjecture false?

A $-4 - (-5) = 1$

B $-7 + 6 = -1$

C $-3 + 6 = 3$

D $-5 + (-5) = -10$

A **net** is a two-dimensional representation of a three-dimensional figure. The net of a solid can be folded to form a three-dimensional figure.

To construct the net of a solid, think of how the figure would look if you unfolded it face by face.

To determine the solid figure formed by a net, look at the shapes and number of faces in the net.

Here are the 11 nets for a cube. Think about how you would fold each into a cube.

You can use a net to find the surface area of a solid figure. Find the area of each face. Then add the areas.

🟊 GUIDED PRACTICE

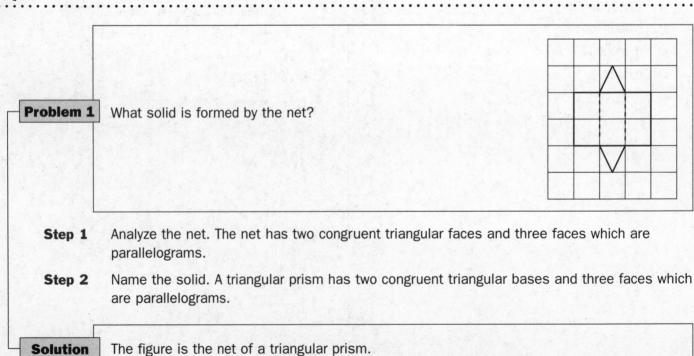

Problem 1   What solid is formed by the net?

Step 1   Analyze the net. The net has two congruent triangular faces and three faces which are parallelograms.

Step 2   Name the solid. A triangular prism has two congruent triangular bases and three faces which are parallelograms.

Solution   The figure is the net of a triangular prism.

🔷 **ADDITIONAL PROBLEMS**

Problem 2

Marla said the figure at right is the net of a triangular pyramid. Explain why Marla is incorrect and correctly name the solid formed by the net. Then draw a net of a triangular pyramid.

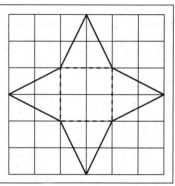

Step 1 Analyze the net. The net has four congruent triangular faces and one face that is a(n) _____.

Step 2 Name the solid. The solid is a(n) _____.

Step 3 Explain why Marla is incorrect. A net of a triangular pyramid has _____ faces that are all _____.

Step 4 Draw a net of a triangular pyramid.

Solution

Marla is incorrect because a net of a triangular pyramid has _____ faces that are all _____.
The original figure is a net of a _____.

Problem 3

Find the surface area of the cylinder by finding the sum of the areas of the faces. Round to the nearest hundredth.

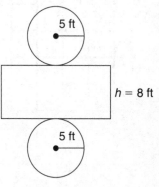

Step 1 Find the area of one of the circular faces using the formula for the area of a circle. _____

Step 2 Find the area of one of the rectangular lateral faces. The length of the lateral face is the circumference of the bases. The width of the lateral face is the height of the cylinder. _____

Step 3 Add the areas.

2(_____)ft^2 + _____ ft^2 = _____ ft^2

Solution The surface area of the cylinder is _____ ft^2.

SHORT ANSWER QUESTIONS

Draw 3 different nets for a cube.

1.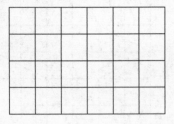

2.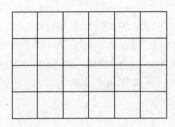

3.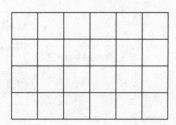

Name the solid that is formed by each net.

4.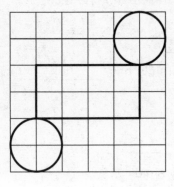

_____

5.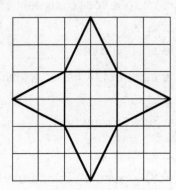

_____

6.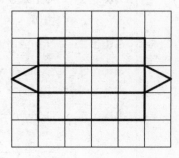

_____

7.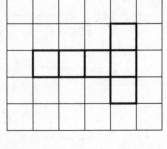

_____

8.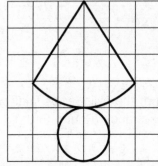

_____

9.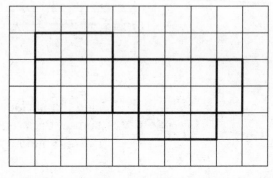

_____

List each shape and number of faces for each solid figure.

10. cube _____

11. triangular pyramid _____

12. cylinder _____

13. rectangular prism _____

14. Explain how you could use a net to find the surface area of a square pyramid.

STAAR PRACTICE

. . . .

DIRECTIONS   Read each question. Then circle the letter for the correct answer.
If a correct answer is <u>not here</u>, circle the letter for "Not Here."

1   Use the figure below to answer the question.

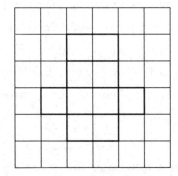

What solid is formed by the net?

A   Cube   **C**   Rectangular pyramid

B   Rectangular prism   **D**   Triangular prism

2   Use the figure below to answer the question.

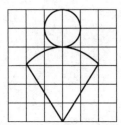

What solid is formed by the net?

A   Cone   **C**   Triangular pyramid

B   Cylinder   **D**   Sphere

3   Use the figure below to answer the question.

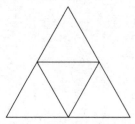

What solid is formed by the net?

A   Cone   **C**   Triangular pyramid

B   Rectangular prism   **D**   Triangular prism

4   Use the figure below to answer the question.

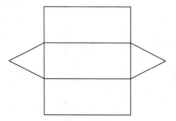

What solid is formed by the net?

A   Cube   **C**   Triangular pyramid

B   Rectangular prism   **D**   Triangular prism

5   What is the surface area of the cylinder, in square inches? Round to the nearest hundredth.

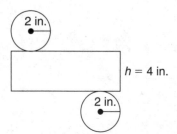

Record your answer and fill in the bubbles on the grid below. Be sure to use the correct place value.

★ STAAR PRACTICE: CUMULATIVE

DIRECTIONS Read each question. Then circle the letter for the correct answer. If a correct answer is <u>not here</u>, circle the letter for "Not Here."

6 Which shows a line in hyperbolic geometry?

A

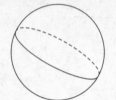

B

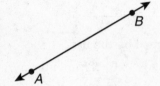

C

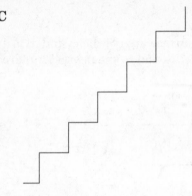

D

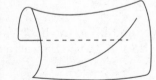

7 Use the pattern below to answer the question.

0, 1, 4, 13, 40

Which is the 9th number in the pattern?

A 148

B 1093

C 3240

D 3280

8 In which two systems of geometry could a depiction of a rectangle look the same?

A Taxicab geometry and hyperbolic geometry

B Euclidian geometry and taxicab geometry

C Spherical geometry and Euclidian geometry

D Hyperbolic geometry and spherical geometry

9 Use the diagram below to answer the question.

$n = 1$ $n = 2$ $n = 3$ $n = 4$

1 part   3 parts   7 parts   13 parts

How many parts will there be in the next term in the sequence?

A 5

B 8

C 19

D 21

An **orthographic view** of a solid figure shows a two-dimensional representation of the front, top, and right side of the solid.

To draw the orthographic views, imagine you are looking directly at the figure from the front, top, and right side.

The drawings at right show the orthographic views of the solid.

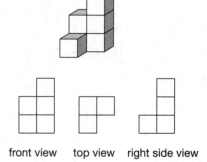

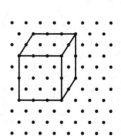

front view   top view   right side view

An **isometric view** shows three sides of a solid figure from a corner view of the solid.

An isometric drawing makes the solid look three dimensional. You can use isometric dot paper to draw isometric views of three dimensional figures.

An isometric view of a cube is shown at right.

GUIDED PRACTICE

Problem 1   Draw an isometric view of a rectangular prism with a base 4 units by 3 units and a height of 2 units.

Step 1   Use isometric graph paper. Draw a base 4 units long and 3 units wide.

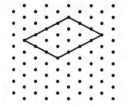

Step 2   From each vertex draw segments 2 units long.

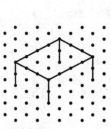

Step 3   Draw the second base by joining the segments drawn in Step 2.

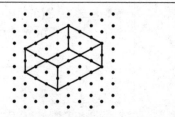

Solution   The isometric view is shown at right.

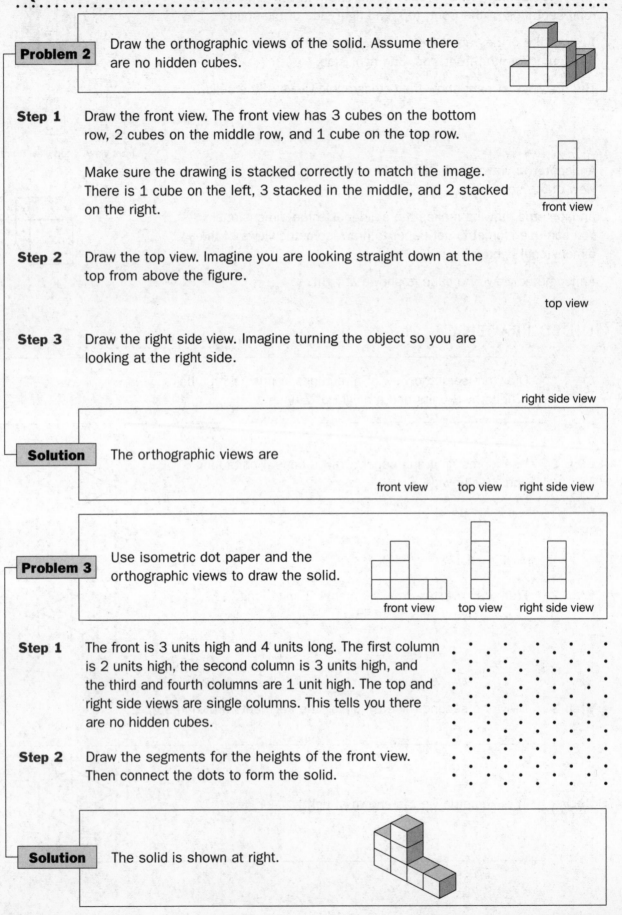

🤠 ADDITIONAL PROBLEMS

Problem 2   Draw the orthographic views of the solid. Assume there are no hidden cubes.

Step 1   Draw the front view. The front view has 3 cubes on the bottom row, 2 cubes on the middle row, and 1 cube on the top row.

Make sure the drawing is stacked correctly to match the image. There is 1 cube on the left, 3 stacked in the middle, and 2 stacked on the right.

front view

Step 2   Draw the top view. Imagine you are looking straight down at the top from above the figure.

top view

Step 3   Draw the right side view. Imagine turning the object so you are looking at the right side.

right side view

Solution   The orthographic views are

front view   top view   right side view

Problem 3   Use isometric dot paper and the orthographic views to draw the solid.

front view   top view   right side view

Step 1   The front is 3 units high and 4 units long. The first column is 2 units high, the second column is 3 units high, and the third and fourth columns are 1 unit high. The top and right side views are single columns. This tells you there are no hidden cubes.

Step 2   Draw the segments for the heights of the front view. Then connect the dots to form the solid.

Solution   The solid is shown at right.

★ SHORT ANSWER QUESTIONS

Use dot paper to draw an isometric view of each rectangular prism with the given dimensions.

1. Base: 5 × 3 units
height: 2 units

2. Base: 3 × 3 units
height: 3 units

3. Base: 6 × 2 units
height: 4 units

Draw the indicated orthographic view of the figure shown to the left.

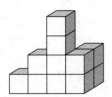

4.

_____
front

5.

_____
top

6.

_____
side

7.

_____
front

8.

_____
top

9.

_____
side

10.

_____
front

11.

_____
top

12.

_____
side

13. Use the orthographic views to draw the solid on the isometric dot paper.

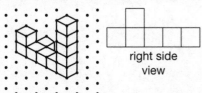

front view   top view   right side
view

14. Gary drew the right side view of the solid figure. Explain why Gary's answer is
incorrect. Then draw the correct orthographic view.

right side
view

_____

_____

_____

_____
correct side
view

STAAR PRACTICE

DIRECTIONS Read each question. Then circle the letter for the correct answer. If a correct answer is <u>not here</u>, circle the letter for "Not Here."

1   Look at the figure below.

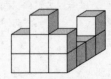

Which shows the right side view of the solid? Assume there are no hidden cubes.

A   **C**

B   **D**   Not here

2   Look at the figure below.

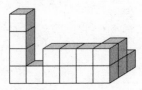

Which shows the top view of the solid? Assume there are no hidden cubes.

A

B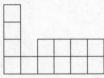

C

D   Not here

3   Which shows the isometric view of a rectangular prism with a base of 3 units by 2 units and a height of 4 units?

A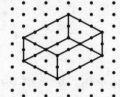

B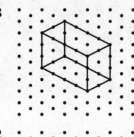

C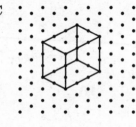

D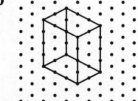

4 Look at the figures below.

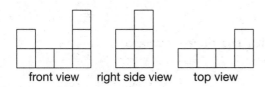

front view   right side view   top view

Which isometric view shows the solid described by the orthographic views?

A

B

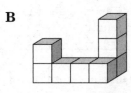

C

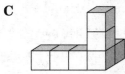

D

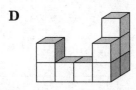

5 Look at the figure below.

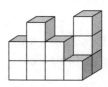

How many squares will show on the orthographic right side view of this figure?

Record your answer and fill in the bubbles on the grid below. Be sure to use the correct place value.

★ STAAR PRACTICE: CUMULATIVE

DIRECTIONS   Read each question. Then circle the letter for the correct answer. If a correct answer is <u>not here</u>, circle the letter for "Not Here."

6   Look at the net below.

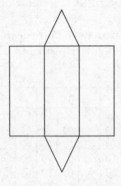

What solid is formed by the net?

A   Cone

B   Rectangular pyramid

C   Triangular prism

D   Triangular pyramid

7   In which situation could you use geometric principles to solve the problem?

A   Determining the height of a pyramid by using the length of your shadow

B   Determining the speed of a train by using the distance and time between stops

C   Determining the capacity of the stadium by using the number of rows and number of seats per row

D   Determining when two buses will return to the station at the same time, using the number of minutes for each route

8   Use the Law of Syllogism to select a valid conclusion from the statements below.

> Given: A regular polygon is a polygon in which all angles are equal and all sides have the same length.
>
> An equilateral triangle has 3 equal angles and 3 sides that are the same length.

A   A regular polygon is an equilateral triangle.

B   An equilateral polygon is a triangle.

C   A triangle is an equilateral polygon.

D   An equilateral triangle is a regular polygon.

9   Use the table to answer the question.

Figure	△	□	⬠	⬡	⬣
Number of Edges(n)	3	4	5	6	7
Sum of Interior Angles	180°	360°	540°	720°	900°

Which expression could you use to determine the sum of the interior angles of a polygon, based on the number of edges, n?

A $(180 \times n) - 2$

B $(n - 2) \times 180$

C $180 + (n - 2)$

D $(n + 2) \times 180$

The **coordinate plane** is a **coordinate system** formed by the intersection of two number lines. The horizontal number line is the *x*-axis and the vertical number line is the *y*-axis.

All points on the plane can be identified by an **ordered pair**. The coordinates of the ordered pair tell the location of the point on the plane.

You can use the coordinate plane to solve many types of geometric problems.

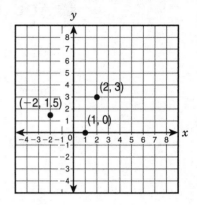

 GUIDED PRACTICE

Problem 1 Graph $\overline{AB}$ with endpoints (−5, 4) and (2, 4) and $\overline{CD}$ with endpoints (1, 1) and (1 −6). Are the segments congruent?

Step 1 Graph $\overline{AB}$. Plot the point (−5, 4) and label it A. Then plot the point (2, 4) and label is B. $\overline{AB}$ is a horizontal segment.

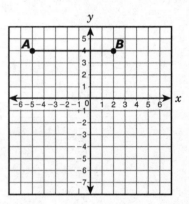

Step 2 Graph $\overline{CD}$. Plot the point (1, 1) and label it C. Then plot the point (1, −6) and label it D. $\overline{CD}$ is a vertical segment.

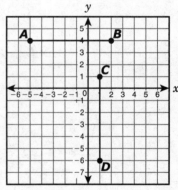

Step 3 Because the segments are horizontal and vertical, you can count the number of units to find their length. $AB = 7$ and $CD = 7$. The segments are of equal length, so they are congruent.

Solution $\overline{AB}$ and $\overline{CD}$ are congruent.

✦ ADDITIONAL PROBLEMS
....

Problem 2

Plot the points $D(2, 5)$, $E(0, 0)$, and $F(2, -6)$. Then draw $\angle DEF$. Classify the angle as acute, right, obtuse, or straight.

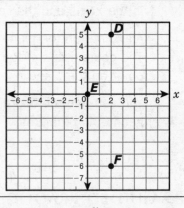

Step 1 Plot each point.

Step 2 Draw $\angle DEF$.

Step 3 The angle measure is greater than 90°. Classify the angle. _____

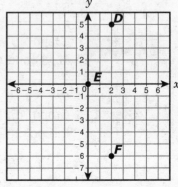

Solution The angle is _____.

Problem 3

Find the area of a triangle ABC with vertices $A(-2, 5)$, $B(-2, -1)$, and $C(6, -1)$.

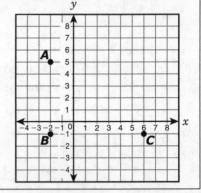

Step 1 Plot each point.

Step 2 Connect the points to draw a triangle. The triangle is a right triangle.

Step 3 Count the number of units for the base and height. Then use the formula for the area of a triangle to calculate the area. _____

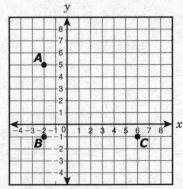

Solution The area of the triangle is _____ square units.

SHORT ANSWER QUESTIONS

Plot and label each ordered pair on the coordinate plane.

1. A(–4, 2)

2. B(–4, –5)

3. C(7, –5)

4. D(7, –1)

5. E(4, 6)

6. F(–2, 6)

7. G(2, 1)

8. H(7, 4)

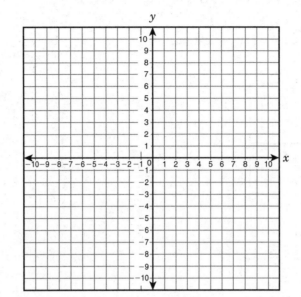

Use the points you plotted on the coordinate plane to answer Questions 9–15. For Questions 9–12, describe each angle as acute, obtuse, right, or straight.

9. ∠ABC _____

10. ∠CDG _____

11. ∠EFG _____

12. ∠HDC _____

13. What is the area of △DCB? _____

14. John said segment CD is $\frac{2}{3}$ the length of segment EF. Is John correct? Explain.

_____

15. Madeline wants to plot a rectangle on the coordinate plane. If she uses points B, C, and H, where should she plot the fourth point? Explain. What will be the perimeter and area of Madeline's rectangle?

_____

_____

_____

STAAR PRACTICE

DIRECTIONS Read each question. Then circle the letter for the correct answer. If a correct answer is <u>not here</u>, circle the letter for "Not Here."

1 Use the graph below to answer the question.

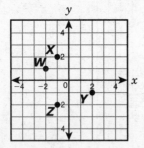

Which point is located at $(-1, 2)$?

A Point W

B Point X

C Point Y

D Point Z

2 Points A, B, and C are plotted on a coordinate plane. Point A is located at $(3, 2)$. Point B is located at $(-1, 4)$. Point C is located at $(5, -2)$. How would you classify angle ABC?

A Acute

B Obtuse

C Right

D Straight

3 Points P, Q, and R are plotted on a coordinate plane. Point P is located at $(-2, -3)$. Point Q is located at $(4, -3)$. Point R is located at $(4, 2)$. What is the area, in square units, of triangle PQR?

A 11

B 15

C 24

D 30

4 Karly plotted point J at $(-4, 5)$ on a coordinate plane. She will plot point K at $(3, -4)$. Where will K be in relation to J?

A 3 units to the right and 4 units down

B 0 units to the right and 2 units down

C 4 units to the right and 5 units down

D 7 units to the right and 9 units down

5 Points C, D, E, and F are plotted on a coordinate plane.

> Point C is located at $(-3, 2)$.
> Point D is located at $(4, 2)$.
> Point E is located at $(-1, 5)$.
> Point F is located at $(-1, -3)$.

What is the difference in length between EF and CD?

Record your answer and fill in the bubbles on the grid below. Be sure to use the correct place value.

STAAR PRACTICE: CUMULATIVE

DIRECTIONS Read each question. Then circle the letter for the correct answer. If a correct answer is <u>not here</u>, circle the letter for "Not Here."

6 Use the figure below to answer the question.

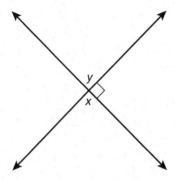

Which of the following is a true statement?

A ∠x and ∠y are supplementary.

B ∠x and ∠y are complementary.

C ∠x and ∠y are supplementary and complementary.

D ∠x and ∠y are neither supplementary nor complementary.

7 Brian made a conjecture that for all real numbers, $\frac{1}{2}n \leq n$. Which is a counterexample that proves Brian's conjecture is false?

A $n = -2$ **C** $n = 1$

B $n = 0$ **D** $n = 2$

8 Which shows a representation of a triangle on a plane in Euclidian geometry?

A
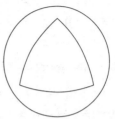

B
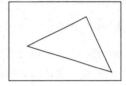

C
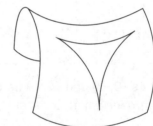

D
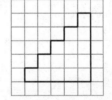

9 A triangle has one angle that measures 36°. The other two angles are congruent. What are the angle measures of the triangle?

A 36°, 36°, 36°   **C** 36°, 36°, 108°

B 36°, 144°, 144°   **D** 36°, 72°, 72°

The **slope** of a line is the steepness of the line.

The slope m of a line containing the points (x_1, y_1) and (x_2, y_2) is found

using the formula $m = \frac{y_2 - y_1}{x_2 - x_1}$. If $x_2 = x_1$, then the slope is undefined.

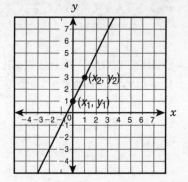

Slope-intercept form for the equation of a line:

The equation of a line with slope m and y-intercept b is $y = mx + b$.
If the slope of a line is 2 and the y-intercept is -1, the equation of the
line in slope-intercept form is $y = 2x - 1$.

Point-slope form for the equation of a line:

The equation of a line with slope m containing the point (x_1, y_1) is $y - y_1 = m(x - x_1)$.
If the slope of a line is 4 and the line contains the point $(3, -5)$, the equation of the
line in point-slope form is $y + 5 = 4(x - 3)$.

Two lines are **parallel** if and only if they have the same slope.

Two lines are **perpendicular** if and only if the product of their slopes is -1. In other words,
their slopes are negative reciprocals.

🐾 GUIDED PRACTICE

Problem 1

Points $(0, 3)$ and $(4, 5)$ lie on $\overleftrightarrow{AB}$. Points $(2, 0)$ and $(6, 2)$ lie on $\overleftrightarrow{CD}$.
Determine whether $\overleftrightarrow{AB}$ and $\overleftrightarrow{CD}$ are parallel.

Step 1   Find the slope of $\overleftrightarrow{AB}$.

$$m = \frac{y_2 - y_1}{x_2 - x_1}$$

$$= \frac{5 - 3}{4 - 0}$$

$$= \frac{2}{4} \text{ or } \frac{1}{2}$$

Step 2   Find the slope of $\overleftrightarrow{CD}$.

$$m = \frac{y_2 - y_1}{x_2 - x_1}$$

$$= \frac{2 - 0}{6 - 2}$$

$$= \frac{2}{4} \text{ or } \frac{1}{2}$$

Solution   The slopes are equal so $\overleftrightarrow{AB}$ and $\overleftrightarrow{CD}$ are parallel.

Measuring Up® to the Geometry End-of-Course Exam

★ **ADDITIONAL PROBLEMS**
. . . .

Problem 2   Write the equation of a line that is perpendicular to the line $y = -3x + 1$ through the point (2, 5) in slope-intercept form.

Step 1   Find the slope of the line $y = -3x + 1$. The equation of the line is written in slope-intercept form, so the slope of the line is −3.

Step 2   Determine the slope of the line that is perpendicular to $y = -3x + 1$.

The slope is the negative reciprocal of −3, so the slope is _____.

Step 3   You know the slope and a point on the perpendicular line, so use point-slope form to write the equation of the line.

$$y - y_1 = m(x - x_1)$$

$$y - 5 = \underline{\hspace{1cm}}(x - \underline{\hspace{1cm}})$$

Step 4   Write the equation of the line in slope-intercept form.

Solution   The equation of the perpendicular line is _____.

Problem 3   Determine whether $\overline{CD}$ is an altitude of triangle *ABC*.

Step 1   Find the slope of the line containing $\overline{CD}$.
The line contains the points (1, −4) and (6, 1).

$m = $ _____

Step 2   Find the slope of the line containing $\overline{AB}$.
The line contains the points (3, 6) and (9, −4).

$m = $ _____

Step 3   Determine whether the slopes are negative reciprocals.

Solution   The slopes are/are not _____ negative reciprocals of each other, so $\overline{CD}$ is/is not _____ an altitude of triangle *ABC*.

SHORT ANSWER QUESTIONS

Determine the slope of the line passing through the points. Write the equation of the line in point-slope form.

1. Points (1, 2) and (2, 5) lie on $\overleftrightarrow{XY}$. _____ _____

2. Points (1, 1) and (5, −7) lie on $\overleftrightarrow{JK}$. _____ _____

3. Points (−4, 1) and (8, 4) lie on $\overleftrightarrow{EF}$. _____ _____

4. Points (−4, 2) and (2, −7) lie on $\overrightarrow{PQ}$. _____ _____

Determine if the lines passing through the given points are parallel.

5. Points (−2, −3) and (3, 7) lie on $\overleftrightarrow{GH}$. Points (−4, 9) and (1, −1) lie on $\overleftrightarrow{JK}$. _____

6. Points (−3, 7) and (5, −1) lie on $\overleftrightarrow{AB}$. Points (−1, 1) and (4, −4) lie on $\overleftrightarrow{CD}$. _____

7. Points (−6, 0) and (6, 6) lie on $\overleftrightarrow{LM}$. Points (−8, −3) and (4, 3) lie on $\overrightarrow{PO}$. _____

Determine if the lines passing through the given points are perpendicular.

8. Points (−1, 2) and (2, 8) lie on $\overleftrightarrow{EF}$. Points (0, 3) and (2, 2) lie on $\overleftrightarrow{GH}$. _____

9. Points (0, −2) and (2, 6) lie on $\overrightarrow{PQ}$. Points (−4, −3) and (4, −1) lie on $\overleftrightarrow{RS}$. _____

10. Points (−1, 4) and (2, 5) lie on $\overleftrightarrow{WX}$. Points (−6, −1) and (−9, 0) lie on $\overleftrightarrow{YZ}$. _____

Write the equation of a line in point-slope form that is perpendicular to the given line and passes through the given point.

11. line $y = -2x + 5$

point (8, 1)

_____

12. line $y = \frac{1}{3}x - 2$

point (−1, 7)

_____

13. line $y = -\frac{4}{3}x - 2$

point (−4, −7)

_____

14. How can you use properties of slopes to determine if a parallelogram is a rectangle?

_____

_____

_____

_____

_____

_____

⬥ STAAR PRACTICE

DIRECTIONS   Read each question. Then circle the letter for the correct answer.
If a correct answer is <u>not here</u>, circle the letter for "Not Here."

1   Which equation is the equation of a line that passes through (2, 6) and is parallel to line $y = 5x - 4$?

A $y = -5x + 4$

B $y = 5x - 4$

C $y = -\frac{1}{5}x + 1$

D $y = 5x + 2$

2   Which equation is the equation of a line that passes through (3, 2) and is perpendicular to line $y = -3x - 1$?

A $y - 3 = \frac{1}{3}(x - 2)$

B $y - 2 = \frac{1}{3}(x - 3)$

C $y - 3 = -3(x - 2)$

D $y - 2 = -3(x - 3)$

3   Use the figure below to answer the question.

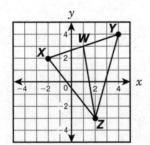

Which is a true statement?

A ZW is an altitude of $\triangle XYZ$ because the slopes of XY and ZW are negative reciprocals.

B ZW is an altitude of $\triangle XYZ$ because the slopes of XY and ZW are congruent.

C ZW is not an altitude of $\triangle XYZ$ because the slopes of XY and ZW are not negative reciprocals.

D ZW is not an altitude of $\triangle XYZ$ because the slopes of XY and ZW are not congruent.

4   Which describes a method you could use to determine if a figure on a coordinate plane is a non-rectangular parallelogram?

A   Determine if the slopes of opposite sides are congruent.

B   Determine if the slopes of adjacent sides are congruent.

C   Determine if the slopes of opposite sides are negative reciprocals.

D   Determine if the slopes of adjacent sides are negative reciprocals.

5 AB passes through points (−4, 4) and (6, 9). What is the slope of a line that is perpendicular to AB?

Record your answer and fill in the bubbles on the grid below. Be sure to use the correct place value.

★ STAAR PRACTICE: CUMULATIVE

DIRECTIONS Read each question. Then circle the letter for the correct answer.
If a correct answer is <u>not here</u>, circle the letter for "Not Here."

6 What is the area, in square units, of a triangle with vertices (−4, −2), (3, 3), and (3, −2)?

   A 17.5

   B 24

   C 35

   D 48

7 Use the figure below to answer the question.

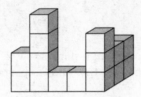

Which shows the top view of the solid? Assume there are no hidden cubes.

   A

   B

   C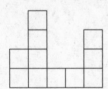

   D Not Here

8 Julia plotted point A at (−4, 1), point B at (1, 4), and point C at (1, −1). Where could she plot point D so $\overline{AD}$ is congruent to $\overline{BC}$?

   A (−4, −3)

   B (6, −4)

   C (1, 4)

   D (1, 1)

9 Use the diagram below to answer the question.

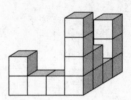

Which shows the top view of the solid? Assume there are no hidden cubes.

   A

   C

   B

   D

The **midpoint** of a segment divides the segment into two congruent segments.

The midpoint M of a segment $\overline{AB}$ with endpoints (x_1, y_1) and (x_2, y_2) is found using the Midpoint Formula:

$$M\left(\frac{x_1 + x_2}{2}, \frac{y_1 + y_2}{2}\right)$$

The **distance** between two points is the length of the line segment connecting the points.

The distance d between two points (x_1, y_1) and (x_2, y_2) is found using the Distance Formula:

$$d = \sqrt{((x_2 - x_1)^2 + (y_2 - y_1)^2)}$$

 GUIDED PRACTICE

· ·

| Problem 1 | Derive the Distance Formula. |

Step 1   Draw a segment with endpoints (x_1, y_1) and (x_2, y_2).

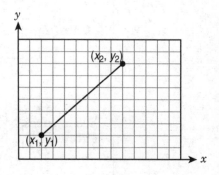

Step 2   Draw a right triangle. The height of the triangle is $y_2 - y_1$ and the base is $x_2 - x_1$.

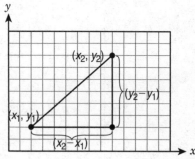

Step 3   Use the Pythagorean Theorem to find the length of the hypotenuse, which is the distance between (x_1, y_1) and (x_2, y_2).

$$a^2 + b^2 = c^2$$

$$(x_2 - x_1)^2 + (y_2 - y_1)^2 = c^2$$

$$\sqrt{((x_2 - x_1)^2 + (y_2 - y_1)^2)} = c$$

The distance d between two points (x_1, y_1) and (x_2, y_2) is found using the formula:

| Solution |

$$d = \sqrt{((x_2 - x_1)^2 + (y_2 - y_1)^2)}$$

🐾 ADDITIONAL PROBLEMS
. . . .

Problem 2 | The midpoint of $\overline{AB}$ is $M(2, -1)$. The coordinates of point A are $(5, -3)$. Find (x, y), the coordinates of point B.

Step 1 Use the Midpoint Formula.

$$(2, -1) = \left(\frac{5 + x}{2}, \frac{-3 + y}{2}\right)$$

Step 2 Set the x coordinates equal and solve for x.

$$2 = \frac{5 + x}{2}$$
$$4 = 5 + x$$
$$-1 = x$$

Step 3 Set the y-coordinates equal and solve for y. _____

Step 4 Write the coordinates of point B. _____

Solution | The coordinates of point B are (_____, _____).

Problem 3 | For a party, Giselle wants to hang a streamer in her rectangular dining room from point A to point B. What is the minimum length of the streamer?

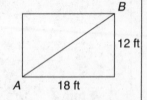

Step 1 Assume point A is at the origin. The coordinates for point A are $(0, 0)$ and the coordinates for point B are (_____, _____).

Step 2 Use the Distance Formula to find AB.

$$d = \sqrt{(\rule{1cm}{0.4pt} - 0)^2 + (\rule{1cm}{0.4pt} - 0)^2}$$

$$= \sqrt{\rule{1.5cm}{0.4pt}^2 + \rule{1.5cm}{0.4pt}^2}$$

$$\approx \rule{1.5cm}{0.4pt} \text{ ft}$$

Step 3 Use the Pythagorean Theorem to check your work.

Solution | The minimum length of the streamer is _____ feet.

SHORT ANSWER QUESTIONS

Find the coordinates of the midpoint of each segment that has the given endpoints.

1. $\overline{AB}$ with endpoints $A(4, 2)$ and $B(-2, -2)$ (_____)

2. $\overline{XY}$ with endpoints $X(3, -1)$ and $Y(7, 5)$ (_____)

3. $\overline{PQ}$ with endpoints $P(5, 9)$ and $Q(-7, 3)$ (_____)

4. $\overline{EF}$ with endpoints $E(-3, -10)$ and $F(6, -1)$ (_____)

Find the length of each segment that has the given endpoints. Round to the nearest hundredth.

5. $\overline{ST}$ with endpoints $S(5, 6)$ and $T(-3, -9)$ _____

6. $\overline{JK}$ with endpoints $J(-1, -1)$ and $K(2, 6)$ _____

7. $\overline{MN}$ with endpoints $M(3, -7)$ and $N(-4, 4)$ _____

8. $\overline{WX}$ with endpoints $W(-7, 1)$ and $X(4, 6)$ _____

Find the hypotenuse of each triangle. Round to the nearest hundredth.

9.

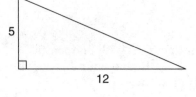

_____

10.

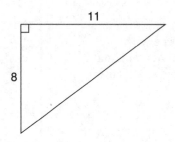

_____

11.

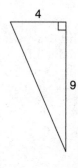

_____

Given the midpoint and one endpoint in Questions 12 and 13, find the missing endpoint.

12. The midpoint of $\overline{CD}$ is $M(2, -1)$. The coordinates of point C are $(-5, 4)$.
What are the coordinates of point D? _____

13. The midpoint of $\overline{UV}$ is $M(3, -8)$. The coordinates of point U are $(8, -5)$.
What are the coordinates of point V? _____

14. Jesse has a rectangular pool that measures 15 feet by 25 feet. He wants to buy a hose that will reach from one corner to the opposite corner plus 20 feet. How can Jesse determine the length of hose he should buy? What is the minimum length, in whole feet, that Jesse should buy?

_____

_____

🔶 **STAAR PRACTICE**

DIRECTIONS Read each question. Then circle the letter for the correct answer. If a correct answer is <u>not here</u>, circle the letter for "Not Here."

1 Use the figure shown below to answer the question.

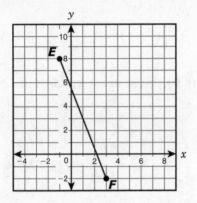

What is the midpoint of $\overline{EF}$?

A (1, 3)   **C** (2, 3)

B (1, 5)   **D** (2, 5)

2 Jill drew $\overline{QR}$ on a coordinate plane with endpoints $(3, -9)$ and $(-3, -1)$. Where should Jill locate point S to divide segment $\overline{QR}$ into two congruent segments?

A (0, −5)   **C** (3, 4)

B (0, 4)   **D** (3, 5)

3 A high school football field measures 160 feet wide by 300 feet long. For a marching band formation, the drum major wants to create a diagonal line from one corner of the field to the opposite corner. What is the length the marchers must cover to form the diagonal across the field?

A 230 feet   **C** 460 feet

B 340 feet   **D** Not Here

4 Use the figure shown below to answer the question.

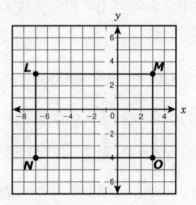

What is the length of $\overline{MN}$? Round your answer to the nearest hundredth.

A 4.12   **C** 12.21

B 10.05   **D** Not Here

5 Determine length of $\overline{GH}$, with endpoints $(5, -12)$ and $(-3, 7)$. Round your answer to the nearest hundredth.

Record your answer and fill in the bubbles on the grid below. Be sure to use the correct place value.

⊕	⊙	⊙	⊙	⊙	⊙	⊙	⊙
⊖	⓪	⓪	⓪	⓪	⓪	⓪	⓪
	①	①	①	①	①	①	①
	②	②	②	②	②	②	②
	③	③	③	③	③	③	③
	④	④	④	④	④	④	④
	⑤	⑤	⑤	⑤	⑤	⑤	⑤
	⑥	⑥	⑥	⑥	⑥	⑥	⑥
	⑦	⑦	⑦	⑦	⑦	⑦	⑦
	⑧	⑧	⑧	⑧	⑧	⑧	⑧
	⑨	⑨	⑨	⑨	⑨	⑨	⑨

 Measuring Up® to the Geometry End-of-Course Exam

STAAR PRACTICE: CUMULATIVE

DIRECTIONS Read each question. Then circle the letter for the correct answer.
If a correct answer is <u>not here</u>, circle the letter for "Not Here."

6 Use the Law of Detachment and the given statements below to draw a valid conclusion.

> Given: If a triangle has a right angle, then the other two angles are acute. Triangle Z has one right angle.

A Triangle Z is a right triangle.

B Triangle Z has exactly one acute angle.

C Triangle Z has exactly two right angles.

D Triangle Z has exactly two acute angles.

7 A plane intersects a sphere at an angle that is 30° to its equatorial diameter. Which of the following shapes describes the intersection?

A Ellipse

B Circle

C Parabola

D Line

8 Use the figure below to answer the question.

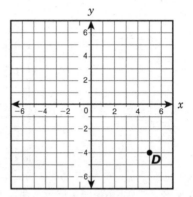

Which ordered pair describes the location of point D on the coordinate plane?

A $(-4, 5)$ **C** $(5, -4)$

B $(4, -5)$ **D** $(5, 4)$

9 Use the figure below to answer the question.

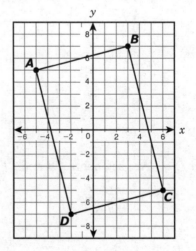

Which is not a true statement?

A $\overline{AB}$ and $\overline{BC}$ are perpendicular.

B $\overline{AD}$ and $\overline{BC}$ are parallel.

C $\overline{AC}$ and $\overline{BD}$ are perpendicular.

D $\overline{AB}$ and $\overline{CD}$ are parallel.

Victoria drew three segments on the coordinate plane.

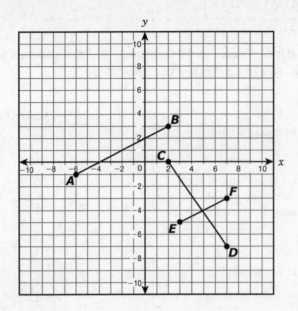

Part A   What are the coordinates of each endpoint of the three segments?

Part B   What are the coordinates of the midpoint of $\overline{AB}$?

Part C   What is the length of each segment?

$\overline{AB}$:

$\overline{CD}$:

$\overline{EF}$:

Part D   Are segments $\overline{AB}$ and $\overline{EF}$ parallel? Justify your answer.

Part E   Are segments $\overline{CD}$ and $\overline{EF}$ perpendicular? Justify your answer.

Nick has a clay cylinder and a clay cone.

Part A   Can Nick cut the cylinder with a flat plane of metal to form a triangle-shaped cross section? How many different cross-section shapes can Nick form?

Part B   Draw the shape that will be formed if Nick cuts the clay cone through the vertex as shown below.

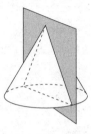

Part C   Draw the net of a cylinder and the net of a cone.

Lesson 12   Patterns

A **pattern** is a set of numbers, words, or figures with a common rule. Here are some examples of patterns:

Numeric Pattern: 2, 4, 6, 8, …

Geometric Pattern: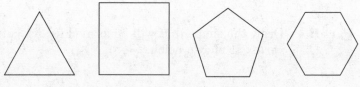

When you are asked to find the next number or figure in a pattern, or to find the rule for a pattern, you are using inductive reasoning to make a conjecture.

 GUIDED PRACTICE

· ·

Problem 1   Describe the rule for the pattern and find the next two figures in the pattern.

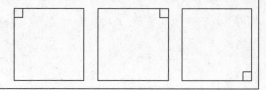

Step 1   Look for a pattern.

In the first figure, the small black square is in the upper left corner of the larger square.

In the second figure, the small black square is in the upper right corner of the larger square.

In the third figure, the small black square is in the bottom right corner of the larger square.

Step 2   Make a conjecture about the rule for the pattern.

Each new figure is rotated 90° to the right (or clockwise.)

Step 3   Draw the next two figures in the pattern.

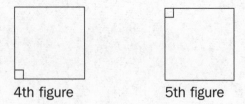

4th figure   5th figure

Solution   The rule for the pattern is: Each new figure is rotated 90° to the right. The next two figures are shown above.

✦ ADDITIONAL PROBLEMS

· ·

Problem 2   Describe the rule for the pattern below and find the next two numbers in the pattern.
−4, 12, −36, 108, ...

Step 1   Look for a pattern.

$$\boxed{-4} \xrightarrow[\times\,(-3)]{} \boxed{12} \xrightarrow[\times\,(-3)]{} \boxed{-36} \xrightarrow[\times\,(-3)]{} \boxed{108}$$

Step 2   Make a conjecture about the rule for the pattern.

Each number in the pattern is _____ times the _____ number.

Step 3   Find the next two numbers in the pattern.

The next two numbers in the pattern are _____ and _____ .

Solution   The rule for the pattern is: _____ .

The next two numbers in the pattern are _____ and _____ .

Problem 3   A diagonal of a polygon connects two nonconsecutive vertices. Use the pattern below to make a conjecture about the number of diagonals from one vertex of an octagon.

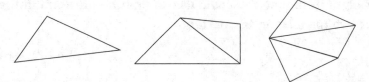

Step 1   Look for a pattern.

A triangle has 3 sides and 0 diagonals.

A quadrilateral has _____ sides and _____ diagonal(s).

A pentagon has _____ sides and _____ diagonal(s).

The number of diagonals from one vertex in each figure is _____ less than the number of sides.

Step 2   Make a conjecture.

An octagon has _____ diagonals from each vertex.

Solution   An octagon has _____ diagonals from each vertex.

SHORT ANSWER QUESTIONS

Describe the rule for each number pattern and find the next two numbers in the pattern.

1. $\frac{1}{2}, \frac{1}{4}, \frac{1}{8}, \frac{1}{16}, \frac{1}{32},$

_____ , _____

2. $-27, 9, -3, 1, -\frac{1}{3},$

_____ , _____

Describe the rule for each geometric pattern. Then find the next two figures in the pattern.

3.

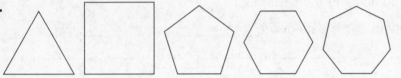

_____   _____ _____

4.

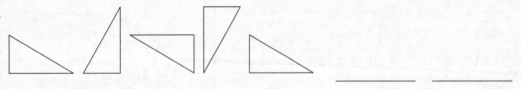

_____ _____

_____

Write a rule for each pattern that you could use to find the *n*th term in the pattern. Then find the next two numbers in the pattern.

5. $\frac{1}{3}, \frac{2}{3}, 1, \frac{4}{3}, \frac{5}{3}$ _____   **6.** $-1, -4, -9, -16, -25$ _____

Use the pattern below to answer Questions 7 and 8. Note: The triangles are not drawn to scale.

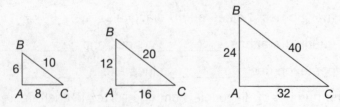

7. Describe the pattern. What are the side lengths of the next two figures in the pattern?

_____

_____

8. Find the perimeter and area of the figures in the pattern. What is the pattern in the perimeters and areas?

_____

_____

★ STAAR PRACTICE

DIRECTIONS Read each question. Then circle the letter for the correct answer.
If a correct answer is <u>not here</u>, circle the letter for "Not Here."

1 Use the numeric pattern to answer the question.

$-16, 4, -1, \dfrac{1}{4}, -\dfrac{1}{16} \ldots$

What is the eighth term in this pattern?

A $-\dfrac{1}{1024}$

C $\dfrac{1}{1024}$

B $-\dfrac{1}{256}$

D $\dfrac{1}{256}$

2 Use the pattern below to answer the question.

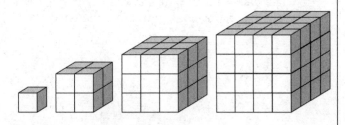

Which expression could you use to find the nth term in this pattern?

A n^3

C $n^2 + 8$

B $8n$

D $4n^2 - 4$

3 Use the pattern below to answer the question.

Figure	△	▱	⬠	⬡	⬡
Number of Vertices (n)	3	4	5	6	7
Number of Triangles	1	2	3	4	5

Which expression could you use to find the number of triangles in an n-gon?

A n

C $n + 2$

B $2n$

D $n - 2$

Use the pattern below to answer Questions 4 and 5.

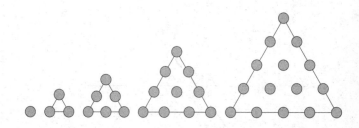

4 Which describes how to find the next figure in the pattern?

A Add 2 to the previous number of dots.

B Add the term numbers to the previous pattern.

C Multiply the term number by 2.

D Square the term number and add 2.

5 How many dots will there be in the 11th term in the pattern?

Record your answer and fill in the bubbles on the grid below. Be sure to use the correct place value.

⊕	⊙	⊙	⊙	⊙	⊙	⊙	⊙
⊖	⓪	⓪	⓪	⓪	⓪	⓪	⓪
	①	①	①	①	①	①	①
	②	②	②	②	②	②	②
	③	③	③	③	③	③	③
	④	④	④	④	④	④	④
	⑤	⑤	⑤	⑤	⑤	⑤	⑤
	⑥	⑥	⑥	⑥	⑥	⑥	⑥
	⑦	⑦	⑦	⑦	⑦	⑦	⑦
	⑧	⑧	⑧	⑧	⑧	⑧	⑧
	⑨	⑨	⑨	⑨	⑨	⑨	⑨

DIRECTIONS Read each question. Then circle the letter for the correct answer. If a correct answer is <u>not here</u>, circle the letter for "Not Here."

6 Use the figure below to answer the question.

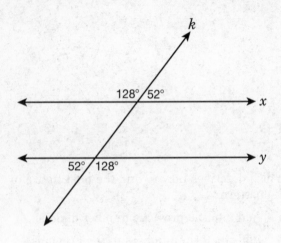

Which of the following is a true statement?

A Line y is a transversal.

B Line x is perpendicular to line k.

C Line x is parallel to line y.

D Not Here

7 Look at the pattern below.

> 3, 12, 48, 192, 768, . . .

What is the 9th number in the pattern?

A 3072

B 12,288

C 49,152

D 196,608

8 A quilt block design is shown below.

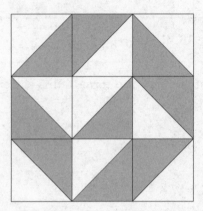

The pattern is a light and dark triangle sewn together to form a square, like the one below.

What transformations would you use to arrange the squares to form the quilt block pattern?

A Dilation and rotation

B Reflection and translation

C Translation and reflection

D Rotation and translation

9 Which is not an example of the historical development of geometric systems?

A Eratosthenes devises a plan to find the Earth's circumference.

B George Hepplewhite designs a chair.

C The problem of the Tunnel of Samos

D Mandelbrot describes the Mandelbrot set to introduce fractals.

Two polygons are **congruent** if they have the same shape and the same size.

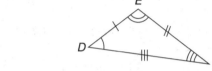

Two polygons are congruent if and only if their corresponding angles and corresponding sides are congruent.

In the figures at right, $\triangle ABC \cong \triangle DEF$. The order of the vertices identifies the corresponding parts of the triangles.

Corresponding angles and corresponding sides are congruent:

$\angle A \cong \angle D; \angle B \cong \angle E; \angle C \cong \angle F$ $\overline{AB} \cong \overline{DE}; \overline{BC} \cong \overline{EF}; \overline{CA} \cong \overline{FD}$

In a **congruence transformation**, the original figure (the preimage) and the transformed figure (the image) are congruent.

You can use the following to prove two triangles are congruent.

SSS Congruence Postulate (Side-Side-Side): If three sides of one triangle are congruent to three sides of another triangle, then the triangles are congruent.

SAS Congruence Postulate (Side-Angle-Side): If two sides and the included angle of one triangle are congruent to two sides and the included angle of another triangle, then the triangles are congruent.

ASA Congruence Postulate (Angle-Side-Angle): If two angles and the included side of one triangle are congruent to two angles and the included side of another triangle, then the triangles are congruent.

AAS Congruence Theorem (Angle-Angle-Side): If two angles and a non-included side of one triangle are congruent to two angles and the corresponding non-included side of another triangle, then the triangles are congruent.

HL Congruence Theorem (Hypotenuse-Leg): If the hypotenuse and a leg of one right triangle are congruent to the hypotenuse and a leg of another right triangle, then the triangles are congruent.

 GUIDED PRACTICE

....

| **Problem 1** | Prove the AAS Congruence Theorem. |

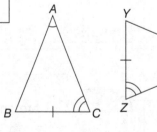

Step 1   Write what is given.
Given: $\angle A \cong \angle X; \angle C \cong \angle Z; \overline{BC} \cong \overline{YZ}$
Prove: $\triangle ABC \cong \triangle XYZ$

Step 2

Statement	Reason
1. $\angle A \cong \angle X; \angle C \cong \angle Z; \overline{BC} \cong \overline{YZ}$	Given
2. $\angle B \cong \angle Y$	Third Angle Theorem
3. $\triangle ABC \cong \triangle XYZ$	AAS Congruence Postulate

| **Solution** | You have proved that if two angles and the non-included side of one triangle are congruent to two angles and the non-included side of another triangle, then the triangles are congruent. |

★ ADDITIONAL PROBLEMS

Problem 2 Show that the reflection of △ABC across the x-axis is a congruence transformation.

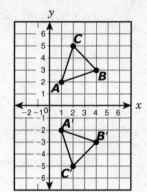

Step 1 Identify the corresponding sides of the triangles.

$\overline{AB}$ corresponds to $\overline{A'B'}$.

$\overline{BC}$ corresponds to $\overline{B'C'}$.

$\overline{CA}$ corresponds to $\overline{C'A'}$.

Step 2 Determine the coordinates of all the vertices.

A (_____ , _____)   A' (_____ , _____)

B (_____ , _____)   B' (_____ , _____)

C (_____ , _____)   C' (_____ , _____)

Step 3 Use the Distance Formula to find each of the following lengths.

$AB = \sqrt{(4-1)^2 + (3-2)^2} = \sqrt{10}$ $A'B' = \sqrt{(4-1)^2 + (-3-(-2))^2} = \sqrt{10}$

$BC = \sqrt{(\underline{} - 4)^2 + (\underline{} - 3)^2} = \underline{}$

$B'C' = \sqrt{(\underline{} - 4)^2 + (\underline{} - (-3))^2} = \underline{}$

$CA = \sqrt{(\underline{} - \underline{})^2 + (\underline{} - \underline{})^2} = \underline{}$

$C'A' = \sqrt{(\underline{} - \underline{})^2 + (\underline{} - \underline{})^2} = \underline{}$

Step 4 By the SSS Congruence Postulate, the triangles are congruent.

Solution The triangles are congruent, so the reflection is a congruence transformation.

Problem 3 Tim needs to replace the mainsail on his sailboat. The old and new sails are shown. Are the sails the same size and shape?

Step 1 Determine what you know.

The sails are shaped like right triangles. The hypotenuses are the same length and the shorter legs are the same length.

Step 2 Draw a conclusion.

By the _____ , the sails are congruent.

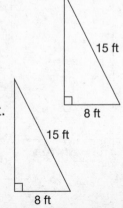

Solution The old and the new sails are the same size and shape.

SHORT ANSWER QUESTIONS

For each pair of triangles, write the Congruence Postulate or Theorem from the box that proves the triangles are congruent.

1.

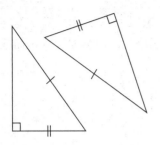

2.

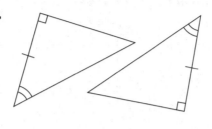

Congruence Postulate or Theorem	
SSS	ASA
SAS	AAS
HL	

_____

_____

3.

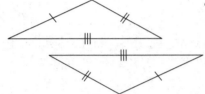

4.

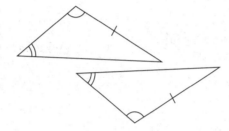

5.

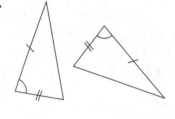

_____

_____

_____

Use the diagram on the coordinate plane to answer Questions 6–8.

6. Identify the corresponding sides of the triangles.

$\overline{AB}$ corresponds to _____.

$\overline{BC}$ corresponds to _____.

$\overline{CA}$ corresponds to _____.

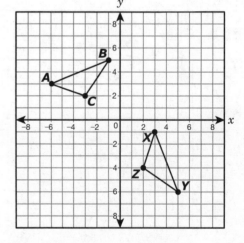

7. Find the length of each side.

$\overline{AB}$: _____ $\overline{XY}$: _____

$\overline{BC}$: _____ $\overline{YZ}$: _____

$\overline{CA}$: _____ $\overline{ZX}$: _____

8. Determine if the triangles are congruent according to one of the Congruence Postulates. Explain.

_____

9. Given $\triangle JKL$ and $\triangle PQR$ in a coordinate plane and $m\angle J$ and $m\angle P$, can you determine whether or not $\triangle JKL \cong \triangle PQR$? Explain.

_____

_____

_____

★ STAAR PRACTICE

....

DIRECTIONS Read each question. Then circle the letter for the correct answer.
If a correct answer is <u>not here</u>, circle the letter for "Not Here."

1 Use the diagram below to answer the question.

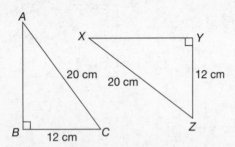

Which Congruence Postulate or Theorem could you use to prove the triangles congruent?

A AAS   **C** HL

B ASA   **D** SAS

2 Use the diagram below to answer the question.

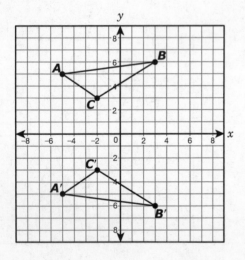

Triangle ABC is reflected over the x-axis. Which statement is true?

A $\triangle ABC \cong \triangle A'B'C'$ by the HL Congruence Theorem.

B $\triangle ABC \cong \triangle A'B'C'$ by the SSS Congruence Postulate.

C $\triangle ABC \cong \triangle A'B'C'$ by the ASA Congruence Postulate.

D $\triangle ABC \not\cong \triangle A'B'C'$.

3 Use the diagram below to answer the question.

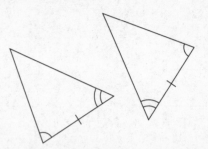

Which Congruence Postulate or Theorem could you use to prove the triangles congruent?

A AAS

B HL

C ASA

D SSS

4 Use the diagram below to answer the question.

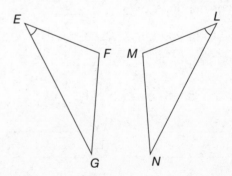

For $\triangle EFG$ and $\triangle LMN$, which is a pair of corresponding sides?

A $\overline{FG}$ and $\overline{MN}$

B $\overline{EF}$ and $\overline{LN}$

C $\overline{EG}$ and $\overline{LM}$

D $\overline{EF}$ and $\overline{MN}$

STAAR PRACTICE

5 Use the diagram below to answer the question.

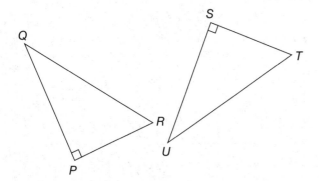

Triangle *PQR* is congruent to △*SUT*. If $\overline{QR}$ measures 35 cm, $\overline{RP}$ measures 21 cm, and $\overline{PQ}$ measures 28 cm, what does $\overline{SU}$ measure, in centimeters?

Record your answer and fill in the bubbles on the grid below. Be sure to use the correct place value.

⊕	⊙	⊙	⊙	⊙	⊙	⊙	⊙
⊖	⓪	⓪	⓪	⓪	⓪	⓪	⓪
	①	①	①	①	①	①	①
	②	②	②	②	②	②	②
	③	③	③	③	③	③	③
	④	④	④	④	④	④	④
	⑤	⑤	⑤	⑤	⑤	⑤	⑤
	⑥	⑥	⑥	⑥	⑥	⑥	⑥
	⑦	⑦	⑦	⑦	⑦	⑦	⑦
	⑧	⑧	⑧	⑧	⑧	⑧	⑧
	⑨	⑨	⑨	⑨	⑨	⑨	⑨

STAAR PRACTICE: CUMULATIVE

DIRECTIONS Read each question. Then circle the letter for the correct answer. If a correct answer is <u>not here</u>, circle the letter for "Not Here."

6 Use the diagram below to answer the question.

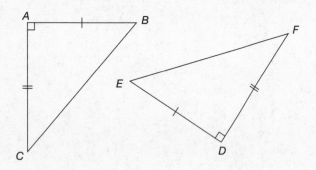

Triangle *ABC* is congruent to △*DEF*. Which two ratios are equal?

A $\dfrac{AB}{BC}$ and $\dfrac{EF}{DE}$

C $\dfrac{BC}{AC}$ and $\dfrac{EF}{DE}$

B $\dfrac{AC}{AB}$ and $\dfrac{DE}{EF}$

D $\dfrac{AB}{AC}$ and $\dfrac{DE}{DF}$

7 Use the diagram below to answer the question.

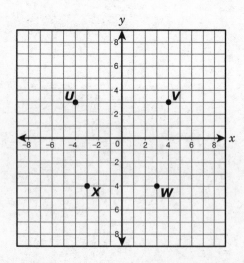

Which ordered pair describes point *W*?

A (−4, 3)

B (−3, −4)

C (3, −4)

D (3, 4)

8 Use the diagram below to answer the question.

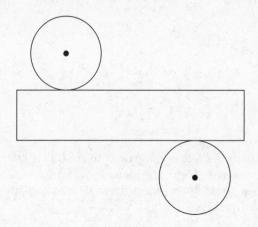

This is the net of which solid figure?

A Cone

B Cylinder

C Hemisphere

D Sphere

9 Which is a true statement?

A Parallel lines intersect at the horizon.

B Perpendicular lines never intersect.

C Parallel lines intersect to form a straight angle.

D Perpendicular lines intersect to form right angles.

A **transformation** changes the position, size, or shape of a figure. A figure before transformation is called the **preimage**. The figure after transformation is called the **image**.

A **translation** moves each point of a figure the same distance and direction.

- A translation along vector ⟨a, b⟩ maps a point in the preimage (x, y) to a point in the image (x + a, y + b).

A **rotation** moves a figure a number of degrees about a fixed point called the **center of rotation**.

- A rotation 90° counterclockwise about the origin maps a point in the preimage (x, y) to a point in the image (−y, x).
- A rotation 180° counterclockwise about the origin maps a point in the preimage (x, y) to a point in the image (−x, −y).

A **reflection** moves a figure across a line called the line of reflection. Each point on the image and its corresponding point on the preimage are the same distance from the line of reflection.

- A reflection across the x-axis maps a point in the preimage (x, y) to a point in the image (x, −y).
- A reflection across the y-axis maps a point in the preimage (x, y) to a point in the image (−x, y).
- A reflection across the y = x maps a point in the preimage (x, y) to a point in the image (y, x).

Translations, reflections, and rotations are **congruence transformations** because the preimage and image are congruent.

 GUIDED PRACTICE

Problem 1 A triangle has vertices A (2, 5), B (3, −1), and C (8, −6). What are the vertices of the image if the figure is reflected across the y-axis?

Step 1 The triangle is reflected across the y-axis, so each point in the preimage maps to (−x, y).

Step 2 Write each vertex of the image.

A(2, 5)→A' (−2, 5)   B(3, −1)→B'(−3, −1)   C(8, −6)→C'(−8, −6)

Solution The vertices of the image are: A'(−2, 5), B'(−3, −1), C'(−8, −6).

✦ ADDITIONAL PROBLEMS

Problem 2   Square *ABCD* is translated along the vector ⟨3,5⟩. Graph the preimage.

Step 1   Identify the coordinates of the vertices of the preimage.

     A(−4, 6)   *B*(−2, 4)   *C*(−4, 2)   *D*(−6, 4)

Step 2   Write each vertex of the image.

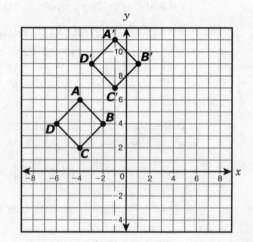

     A(−4, 6)→*A*′(−1, 11)

     B(−2, 4)→*B*′(_____ , _____)

     C(−4, 2)→*C*′(_____ , _____)

     D(−6, 4)→*D*′(_____ , _____)

Step 3   Graph the image on the same coordinate plane.

Solution   The coordinates of the image are *A*′(−1, 11), *B*′(_____ , _____), *C*′(_____ , _____), and *D*′(_____ , _____). See graph above.

Problem 3 $\overline{AB}$ is rotated counterclockwise 90° about the origin. What are the coordinates of the endpoints of the image? Graph the image.

Step 1   Identify the coordinates of the vertices of the preimage.

     A(_____ , _____)   *B*(_____ , _____)

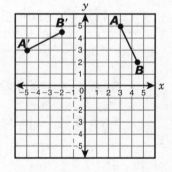

Step 2   Write each vertex of the image.

     A′(_____ , _____)   *B*′(_____ , _____)

Step 3   Graph the image on the same coordinate plane.

Solution   The coordinates of the image are *A*′(_____ , _____) and *B*′(_____ , _____).

SHORT ANSWER QUESTIONS

Use the figures on the coordinate grid to answer Questions 1–12. Perform each transformation on a separate sheet of graph paper, then write the coordinates of the image.

1. Reflect △ABC across the x-axis.
    A′(_____, _____), B′(_____, _____), C′(_____, _____)

2. Translate △ABC along the vector ⟨4, 2⟩.
    A′(_____, _____), B′(_____, _____), C′(_____, _____)

3. Rotate △ABC 180° counterclockwise about the origin.
    A′(_____, _____), B′(_____, _____), C′(_____, _____)

4. Reflect △DEF across the y-axis.
    D′(_____, _____), E′(_____, _____), F′(_____, _____)

5. Translate △DEF along the vector ⟨3, –2⟩.
    D′(_____, _____), E′(_____, _____), F′(_____, _____)

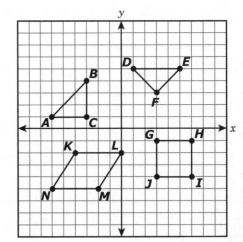

6. Rotate △DEF 90° counterclockwise about the origin. D′(_____, _____), E′(_____, _____),
    F′(_____, _____)

7. Reflect GHIJ across the y = x. G′(_____, _____), H′(_____, _____), I′(_____, _____),
    J′(_____, _____)

8. Translate GHIJ along the vector ⟨–5, 5⟩. G′(_____, _____), H′(_____, _____), I′(_____, _____),
    J′(_____, _____)

9. Rotate GHIJ 90° counterclockwise about the origin. G′(_____, _____), H′(_____, _____),
    I′(_____, _____), J′(_____, _____)

10. Reflect KLMN across the x-axis. K′(_____, _____), L′(_____, _____), M′(_____, _____),
    N′(_____, _____)

11. Translate KLMN along the vector ⟨–6, –4⟩. K′(_____, _____), L′(_____, _____),
    M′(_____, _____), N′(_____, _____)

12. Rotate KLMN 180° counterclockwise about the origin. K′(_____, _____), L′(_____, _____),
    M′(_____, _____), N′(_____, _____)

13. Triangle X′Y′Z′ is located at X′(–3, 7), Y′(2, 5), and Z′(–1, –1). If the preimage was rotated
    90° counterclockwise about the origin, what are the coordinates of the preimage?

    _____

14. Rectangle L′M′N′O′ is located at L′(4, 5), M′(4, –1), N′(–5, –1), and O′(–5, 5). If the preimage was
    translated along the vector ⟨2, –1⟩ and then reflected across the y-axis, what are the coordinates
    of the preimage?

    _____

🟥 **STAAR PRACTICE**

DIRECTIONS Read each question. Then circle the letter for the correct answer. If a correct answer is <u>not here</u>, circle the letter for "Not Here."

1 A triangle has vertices $A(-4, 3)$, $B(3, -5)$, and $C(-3, -4)$. What are the coordinates of B' after a reflection across the y-axis?

  A (3, 5)   **C** (−3, 5)

  B (−5, 3)   **D** (−3, −5)

2 Use the diagram below to answer the question.

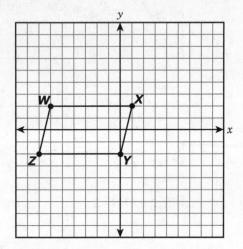

Parallelogram $WXYZ$ is translated along the vector $\langle -2, 4 \rangle$. What are the coordinates of Z'?

  A (−9, 2)

  B (−9, −6)

  C (−5, 2)

  D (−5, −6)

3 Which is a true statement about tessellations?

  A They involve rotations and dilations only.

  B They involve translations and rotations only.

  C They involve translations, rotations, and reflections only.

  D They involve translations, rotations, reflections, and dilations.

Use the diagram below to answer Questions 4 and 5.

4

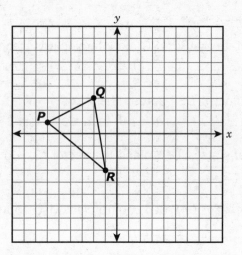

If $\triangle PQR$ is rotated 90° counterclockwise about the origin, what are the coordinates of Q'?

  A (2, 3)   **C** (3, −2)

  B (2, −3)   **D** (−3, −2)

5 If $\triangle PQR$ is reflected across the x-axis, what is the y-coordinate of P'?

Record your answer and fill in the bubbles on the grid below. Be sure to use the correct place value.

⊕	⊙	⊙	⊙	⊙	⊙	⊙	⊙
⊖	⓪	⓪	⓪	⓪	⓪	⓪	⓪
	①	①	①	①	①	①	①
	②	②	②	②	②	②	②
	③	③	③	③	③	③	③
	④	④	④	④	④	④	④
	⑤	⑤	⑤	⑤	⑤	⑤	⑤
	⑥	⑥	⑥	⑥	⑥	⑥	⑥
	⑦	⑦	⑦	⑦	⑦	⑦	⑦
	⑧	⑧	⑧	⑧	⑧	⑧	⑧
	⑨	⑨	⑨	⑨	⑨	⑨	⑨

STAAR PRACTICE: CUMULATIVE

DIRECTIONS Read each question. Then circle the letter for the correct answer.
If a correct answer is <u>not here</u>, circle the letter for "Not Here."

6 Use the diagram below to answer the question.

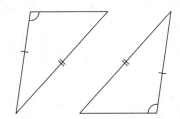

Which Congruence Postulate can be used to prove the triangles congruent?

A AAS

B SSA

C SAS

D SSS

7 Use the figure below to answer the question.

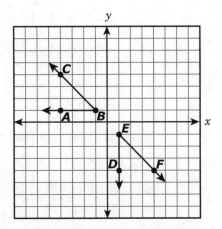

Jen made a conjecture that $\angle ABC$ is congruent to $\angle DEF$. How could she prove that her conjecture is valid?

A Compare the lengths of $\overline{AB}$ and $\overline{BC}$ and the lengths of $\overline{DE}$ and $\overline{EF}$.

B Compare the slopes of $\overline{AB}$ and $\overline{DE}$ and the slopes of $\overline{BC}$ and $\overline{EF}$.

C Use a combination of reflection, rotation, and translation to map $\angle ABC$ onto $\angle DEF$.

D Use a combination of reflections and dilations to map $\angle ABC$ onto $\angle DEF$.

8 A number pattern is shown below.

$$-2, 0, 2, 4, 6$$

Which expression could you use to find any term, n, in the number pattern?

A $2(n - 2)$

B $n + 2$

C $2n - 2$

D $n - 3$

9 Use the pattern below to answer the question.

Term Number (n)	1	2	3	4	5
Figure	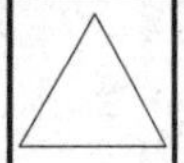 △	▢	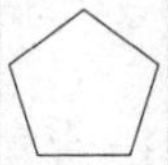 ⬠	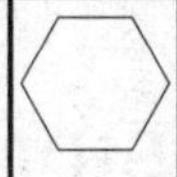 ⬡	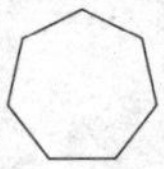 ⬡
Number of Vertices	3	4	5	6	7
Number of Diagonals From One Vertex	0	1	2	3	4

Which expression could you use to find the number of diagonals from one vertex in the nth term in the pattern?

A $n - 1$

B $n - 2$

C $n + 1$

D $n + 2$

A **tessellation** is a collection of one or more figures that cover a plane with no gaps or overlaps.

tessellation

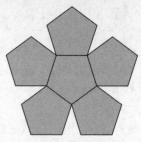

not a tesselation

The sum of the angles around every vertex of a tessellation is 360°.

A **regular tessellation** uses only congruent, regular polygons. A regular polygon tessellates if the sum of its interior angles is a factor of 360°.

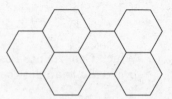

regular tessellation

A **semi-regular** tessellation uses two or more regular polygons.

semi-regular tessellation

🞂 GUIDED PRACTICE

Problem 1

Is the figure a tessellation? Explain why or why not.

If the figure is a tessellation, classify it.

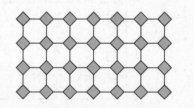

Step 1   Determine whether the figure is a tessellation.

The figure covers the plane with no gaps or overlaps. The figure is a tessellation.

Step 2   Classify the tessellation.

The figure is made up of two regular polygons—a square and an octagon—so it is a semi-regular tessellation.

Solution   The figure is a semi-regular tessellation.

⭐ ADDITIONAL PROBLEMS

Problem 2 Use the tessellation of regular hexagons to show that the sum of the angles around every vertex of a tessellation is 360°.

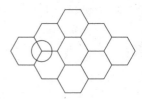

Step 1 Each vertex of the tessellation comprises three interior angles of a regular hexagon. Find the measure of each interior angle of a regular hexagon. The measure of an interior angle of a regular polygon, where *n* is the number of sides, is found using the formula:

$$\frac{(n-2) \times 180°}{n}$$

Use the formula to find the measure of an interior angle. _____

Step 2 Multiply the angle measure by 3. _____

Solution The sum of the angles around every vertex of a regular tessellation of hexagons is _____ .

Problem 3 Describe the transformations you could use to tessellate the trapezoid.

Step 1 Rotate the trapezoid 180° about the point.

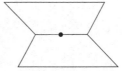

Step 2 Translate the original figure right and then up.

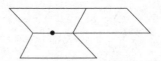

Step 3 Translate the rotated figure right and then down.

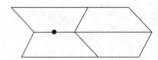

Step 4 Translate the new figure right.

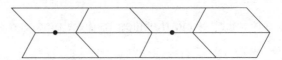

Solution The tessellation was made by rotating the trapezoid and then translating each subsequent part.

⬩ SHORT ANSWER QUESTIONS

Which regular figures will tessellate? Write yes or no.

1.

2.

3.

4.
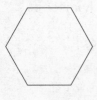

5.

6.

Tell whether each pattern is a regular tessellation (R), semi-regular tessellation (S), or not a tessellation (No).

7.
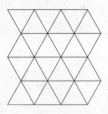

8.
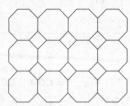

9.
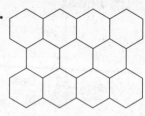

10.
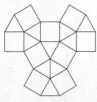

11.
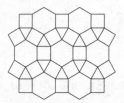

12.
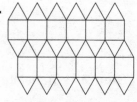

13. Explain why a regular heptagon cannot be used to form a tessellation.

_____

_____

14. Use hexagons and triangles to draw a semi-regular tessellation.

_____

 STAAR PRACTICE

DIRECTIONS Read each question. Then circle the letter for the correct answer.
If a correct answer is <u>not here</u>, circle the letter for "Not Here."

1 Which regular figure will not form a
regular tessellation?

A Hexagon

B Pentagon

C Square

D Triangle

2 Which shows a semi-regular tessellation?

A

B

C

D

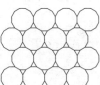

3 What must the sum of the angles around every
vertex measure in order to form a tessellation?

A 90°

B 180°

C 360°

D 720°

4 The eight semi-regular tessellations are formed
by a combination of —

A two different regular polygons.

B three different regular polygons.

C two or three different regular polygons.

D two, three, or four different regular polygons.

5 How many unique regular tessellations can be
formed by symmetrically tiling regular polygons
on a plane?

Record your answer and fill in the bubbles
on the grid below. Be sure to use the correct
place value.

⊕	⊙	⊙	⊙	⊙	⊙	⊙	⊙
⊖	⓪	⓪	⓪	⓪	⓪	⓪	⓪
	①	①	①	①	①	①	①
	②	②	②	②	②	②	②
	③	③	③	③	③	③	③
	④	④	④	④	④	④	④
	⑤	⑤	⑤	⑤	⑤	⑤	⑤
	⑥	⑥	⑥	⑥	⑥	⑥	⑥
	⑦	⑦	⑦	⑦	⑦	⑦	⑦
	⑧	⑧	⑧	⑧	⑧	⑧	⑧
	⑨	⑨	⑨	⑨	⑨	⑨	⑨

★ STAAR PRACTICE: CUMULATIVE

DIRECTIONS Read each question. Then circle the letter for the correct answer.
If a correct answer is <u>not here</u>, circle the letter for "Not Here."

6   Use the figures below to answer the question.

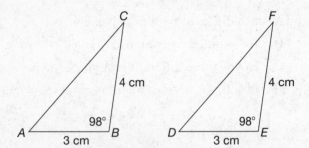

Which is a true statement?

A   The triangles are congruent by SSS.

B   The triangles are congruent by ASA.

C   The triangles are congruent by SAS.

D   The triangles are not congruent.

7   Use the diagram below to answer the question.

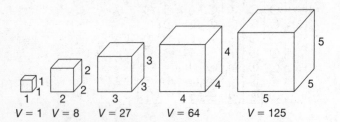

Which algebraic expression describes
the pattern?

A $3n$

B n^3

C $(3n)^3$

D $n^2 + 3$

8   Use the diagram below to answer the question.

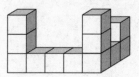

How many squares can you see from the
right side view?

A   6

B   7

C   9

D   14

9   Use the diagram below to answer the question.

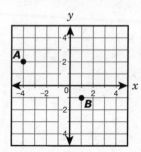

A point at which coordinate would form a right
triangle, along with points A and B?

A $(-4, -1)$

B $(-1, -4)$

C $(1, -4)$

D $(4, -1)$

Lesson 16   Pythagorean Theorem

The Pythagorean Theorem describes the relationship between the hypotenuse and the legs of a right triangle.

A **right triangle** is a triangle with one right angle.

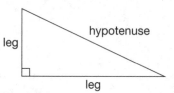

The **hypotenuse** of a right triangle is the side opposite the right angle. It is the longest side of a right triangle.

The **legs** of a right triangle are the sides adjacent to the right angle. They are the two shorter sides of a right triangle.

The **Pythagorean Theorem** states that, in a right triangle, the sum of the squares of the lengths of the legs is equal to the square of the length of the hypotenuse.

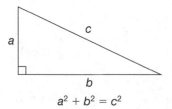

The **converse** of the Pythagorean Theorem is also true. If $a^2 + b^2 = c^2$, then the triangle is a right triangle. In addition, by the Pythagorean Inequalities theorems, if $c^2 > a^2 + b^2$, then the triangle is **obtuse** and if $c^2 < a^2 + b^2$, then the triangle is **acute**.

GUIDED PRACTICE

Problem 1

Two square buildings meet at a right angle. The owners of the buildings want to put a fence along the length of the hypotenuse of the right triangle formed by connecting two corners of the buildings. How many units of fencing are needed?

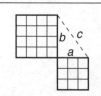

Step 1   Side a is 3 units long and side b is 4 units long. Substitute the values of a and b into the Pythagorean Theorem and solve for c.

$$a^2 + b^2 = c^2$$
$$(3)^2 + (4)^2 = c^2$$
$$9 + 16 = c^2$$
$$25 = c^2$$
$$\sqrt{25} = \sqrt{c^2}$$
$$5 = c$$

Step 2   Notice that a square formed along the length of the hypotenuse has an area of 25 square units. The diagram at right illustrates the Pythagorean Theorem because the sum of the areas of the smaller squares is equal to the area of the square along the hypotenuse. In other words, $a^2 + b^2 = c^2$.

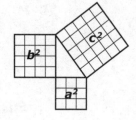

Solution   The length of the hypotenuse is 5 units, so 5 units of fencing are needed.

⭐ **ADDITIONAL PROBLEMS**

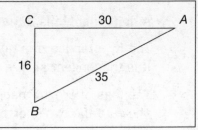

Problem 2   Classify triangle *ABC* as acute, right, or obtuse.

Step 1   The lengths of the two shorter sides of the triangle are 16 and 30.
The length of the longest side is 35.

Step 2   Substitute the side lengths into the Pythagorean Theorem for *a*, *b* and *c*.
Then compare c^2 and $a^2 + b^2$ to classify the triangle.

Solution   Triangle *ABC* is a(n) _____ triangle.

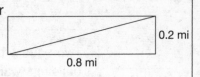

Problem 3   James jogs around the perimeter of a rectangular park and then walks along the diagonal path to cool down. How far does James travel in all? Round your answer to the nearest hundredth.

0.2 mi

0.8 mi

Step 1   The diagonal of a rectangle divides it into two congruent right triangles.
Use the Pythagorean Theorem to find the length of the diagonal path.

$$a^2 + b^2 = c^2$$
$$(\underline{\hspace{1cm}})^2 + (\underline{\hspace{1cm}})^2 = c^2$$
$$\underline{\hspace{1cm}} + \underline{\hspace{1cm}} = c^2$$
$$\underline{\hspace{1cm}} = c^2$$
$$\sqrt{\underline{\hspace{1cm}}} = \sqrt{c^2}$$
$$\underline{\hspace{1cm}} \approx c$$

Step 2   Use the formula for the perimeter of a rectangle to find the perimeter of the park.

$$P = 2l + 2w$$
$$= 2(0.8) + 2(\underline{\hspace{1cm}})$$
$$= 1.6 + \underline{\hspace{1cm}}$$
$$= \underline{\hspace{1cm}}$$

Step 3   Add the length of the diagonal and the perimeter to find the distance James traveled in all.

Solution   James traveled about _____ miles.

SHORT ANSWER QUESTIONS

Use the Pythagorean Theorem to find each missing side length. Write your answers in simplest radical form.

1.

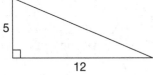

_____

2.

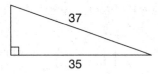

_____

3.

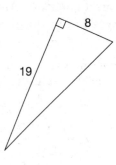

_____

4.

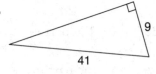

_____

5.

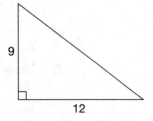

_____

6.

_____

Use the converse of the Pythagorean Theorem and the Pythagorean Inequalities theorems to classify each triangle as acute, right, or obtuse.

7.

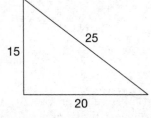

_____

8.

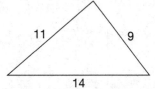

_____

9.

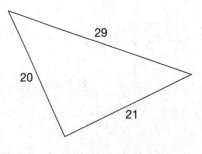

_____

Given _EC_ = 12, use the diagram at right to solve Problems 10 to 12. Round your answers to the nearest hundredth.

10. What is _DC_? _____

11. What is _AD_? _____

12. What is the area of triangle _DAE_? _____ square units

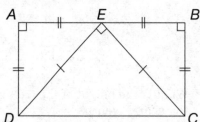

🌟 **STAAR PRACTICE**

DIRECTIONS Read each question. Then circle the letter for the correct answer.
If a correct answer is <u>not here</u>, circle the letter for "Not Here."

1 A right circular cone with a volume of 8π m^3 and a radius of 2 m is shown in the figure.

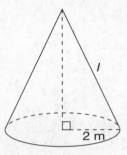

What is the slant height, l, of the cone?

A $2\sqrt{2}$ **C** $2\sqrt{37}$

B $2\sqrt{10}$ **D** Not Here

2 Consider the right triangle.

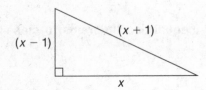

Find the value of x.

A 1   **C** 9

B 4   **D** Not Here

3 An equilateral triangle with side lengths of 5 is shown in the figure.

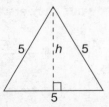

What is the height of the triangle, rounded to the nearest tenth?

A 18.8   **C** 4.3

B 5.6   **D** Not Here

4 An engineer has designed the triangular machine part below.

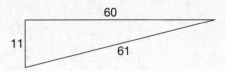

Did the engineer design a right triangular part? Why or why not?

A Yes, since $11^2 + 60^2 = 61^2$, the part is a right triangle.

B No, since $11^2 + 60^2 < 61^2$, the part is an obtuse triangle.

C No, since $11^2 + 60^2 > 61^2$, the part is an acute triangle.

D Not Here

5 Car A begins traveling due north at 11 AM at a constant rate of 50 mph. Car B begins traveling due east $3\frac{1}{2}$ hours after Car A at a constant rate of 65 mph.

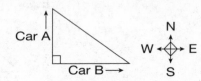

What is the distance at 5 PM between Car A and Car B, rounded to the nearest tenth of a mile?

Record your answer and fill in the bubbles on the grid below. Be sure to use the correct place value.

⊕	⊙	⊙	⊙	⊙	⊙	⊙	⊙
⊖	⓪	⓪	⓪	⓪	⓪	⓪	⓪
	①	①	①	①	①	①	①
	②	②	②	②	②	②	②
	③	③	③	③	③	③	③
	④	④	④	④	④	④	④
	⑤	⑤	⑤	⑤	⑤	⑤	⑤
	⑥	⑥	⑥	⑥	⑥	⑥	⑥
	⑦	⑦	⑦	⑦	⑦	⑦	⑦
	⑧	⑧	⑧	⑧	⑧	⑧	⑧
	⑨	⑨	⑨	⑨	⑨	⑨	⑨

✦ STAAR PRACTICE: CUMULATIVE

DIRECTIONS Read each question. Then circle the letter for the correct answer.
If a correct answer is <u>not here</u>, circle the letter for "Not Here."

6 Study the table.

Number of sides of a polygon (n)	3	4	5	6	7	8	9	n
Number of diagonals drawn from one vertex	0	2	5	9	14	20	27	?

Which of the following is a formula for the
number of possible diagonals drawn from one
vertex in an n–gon?

A $n(n - 1)$

B $\dfrac{n(n - 3)}{2}$

C $\dfrac{n(n - 1)}{2}$

D Not Here

7 Jason made the conjecture below.

> If a number is prime, then the number
> is odd.

Which value is a counterexample to
Jason's conjecture?

A 2

B 5

C 34

D Not Here

8 Consider the figure.

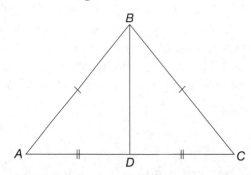

Which theorem or postulate can be used to prove
$\triangle ABD \cong \triangle CBD$?

A ASA   **C** AAS

B SSS   **D** Not Here

9 The regular hexagon *LMNOP* is graphed below.

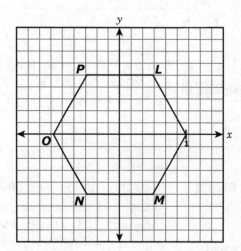

After which transformation will $L'M'N'O'P'$
overlap *LMNOP*?

A A dilation by a factor of 2 with the origin
as the center of dilation

B A 60° rotation counter–clockwise about
the origin

C A transformation 3 units right and
1 unit down

D Not Here

Lesson 17   Special Right Triangles and Pythagorean Triples

The **Pythagorean Theorem** states that, in a right triangle, the sum of the squares of the lengths of the legs is equal to the square of the length of the hypotenuse.

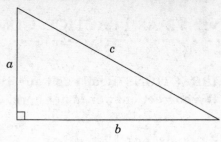

A **Pythagorean triple** is a set of three whole numbers, a, b, c such that $a^2 + b^2 = c^2$. The numbers 3, 4, 5 form a Pythagorean triple because $3^2 + 4^2 = 5^2$.

A **45°–45°–90°** triangle is a right triangle whose acute angles each measure 45°. The legs of a 45°–45°–90° triangle are congruent and the length of the hypotenuse is $\sqrt{2}$ times the length of a leg. You can use this relationship to find the length of the hypotenuse when you know the length of the legs or to find the lengths of the legs when you know the length of the hypotenuse.

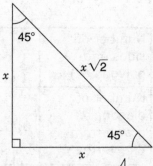

A **30°–60°–90°** triangle is a right triangle whose acute angles are 30° and 60°. The length of the hypotenuse of a 30°–60°–90° triangle is 2 times the length of the shorter leg. The length of the longer leg is $\sqrt{3}$ times the length of the shorter leg. You can use these relationships to find the lengths of the other two sides when you know the length of one side of a 30°–60°–90° triangle.

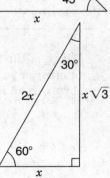

★ GUIDED PRACTICE

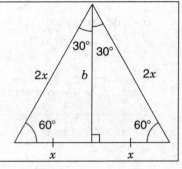

Problem 1   Use the Pythagorean Theorem to show the side relationships in a 30°–60°–90° triangle.

Step 1   Draw the altitude from one vertex of an equilateral triangle with side length 2x to the midpoint of the base opposite. The altitude divides the equilateral triangle into two congruent 30°–60°–90° triangles. The length of the hypotenuse of each triangle is 2 times the length of the shorter leg.

Step 2   Use the Pythagorean Theorem to find the length of the longer leg.

$$a^2 + b^2 = c^2$$
$$(x)^2 + b^2 = (2x)^2$$
$$x^2 + b^2 = 4x^2$$
$$b^2 = 3x^2$$
$$b = x\sqrt{3}$$

Solution   The length of the hypotenuse of a 30°-60°-90° triangle is 2 times the length of the shorter leg. The length of the longer leg is $\sqrt{3}$ times the length of the shorter leg.

🟊 **ADDITIONAL PROBLEMS**

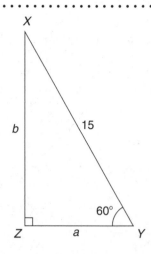

Problem 2	Find the value of *a* and *b* in triangle *XYZ*.

Step 1   Side *a* is the shorter side. The length of the hypotenuse is 2 times the value of *a*. Divide the length of the hypotenuse by 2 to find the value of *a*.

$$15 \div 2 = 7.5$$

Step 2   Side *b* is the longer side. The value of *b* is $\sqrt{3}$ times the length of the shorter side. Multiply the length of the shorter side by $\sqrt{3}$ to find the value of *b*.

$$7.5 \cdot \sqrt{3} = 7.5\sqrt{3}$$

Solution   The value of *a* is 7.5. The value of *b* is $7.5\sqrt{3}$.

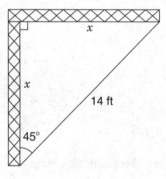

Problem 3	Josh is designing a triangular flower garden. Two sides of the garden are bordered by existing shrubs. What is the area of the garden?

Step 1   In a 45°-45°-90° right triangle, the length of the hypotenuse is $\sqrt{2}$ times the length of the legs. Write and solve an equation representing this relationship.

$$14 = x\sqrt{2}$$

$$\frac{14}{\sqrt{2}} = x$$

$$\frac{\sqrt{2}}{\sqrt{2}} \cdot \frac{14}{\sqrt{2}} = x$$

$$7\sqrt{2} = x$$

Step 2   The legs of a 45°-45°-90° right triangle are the base and height of the triangle. Use the formula for the area of triangle to find the area of the garden.

Solution   The area of the garden is _____ ft².

SHORT ANSWER QUESTIONS

Solve each problem. Leave your answers in simplest radical form.

1.

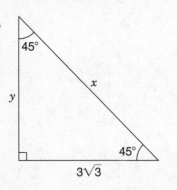

x = _____ y = _____

2.

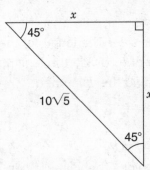

x = _____

3.

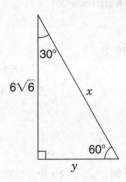

x = _____ y = _____

4.

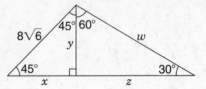

x = _____ y = _____

w = _____ z = _____

5.

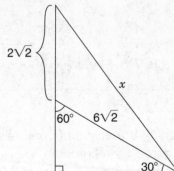

x = _____

6.

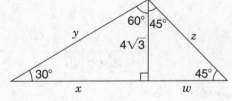

x = _____ y = _____

w = _____ z = _____

Find the perimeter and area. Leave your answers in simplest radical form.

7.

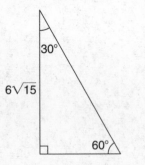

P = _____

A = _____

8.

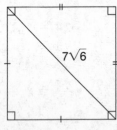

P = _____

A = _____

9.

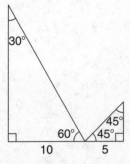

P = _____

A = _____

10. Do the side lengths 33, 56, and 65 form a Pythagorean triple? _____

11. The height of the larger equilateral triangle is $6\sqrt{3}$ and the height of the smaller equilateral triangle is $4\sqrt{3}$. Find the area of the shaded region. Leave your answer in simplest radical form. A = _____

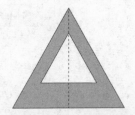

 Measuring Up® to the Geometry End-of-Course Exam

STAAR PRACTICE

DIRECTIONS Read each question. Then circle the letter for the correct answer. If a correct answer is <u>not here</u>, circle the letter for "Not Here."

1 The following numbers and b represent a Pythagorean triple.

$$(9, b, 15)$$

What is the value of b?

A 4

B 5

C 12

D 15

2 Look at the figure.

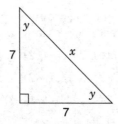

What is the value of y?

A 30°

B 45°

C 60°

D 90°

3 Use the figure below to answer the question.

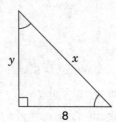

What is the value of x?

A 45   **C** $8\sqrt{3}$

B 16   **D** $8\sqrt{2}$

4 Use the figure below to answer the question.

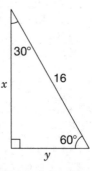

What is the value of x?

A $16\sqrt{3}$

B $16\sqrt{2}$

C $8\sqrt{3}$

D $8\sqrt{2}$

5 Use the figure below to answer the question.

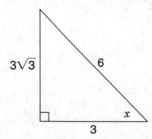

What is the value of x?

A 30°

B 45°

C 60°

D 90°

⭐ STAAR PRACTICE: CUMULATIVE

DIRECTIONS Read each question. Then circle the letter for the correct answer.
If a correct answer is <u>not here</u>, circle the letter for "Not Here."

6 If the hypotenuse of a right triangle measures
17 cm and one of its sides measures 8 cm, what
is the length of the unknown side?

   A 19 cm

   B 15 cm

   C 12 cm

   D 8 cm

7 Use the figure below to answer the question.

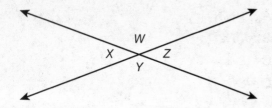

Which of the following statements is true?

   A $Y = Z$

   B $W > X$

   C $X = Z$

   D $Z > X$

8 Use the figure below to answer the question.

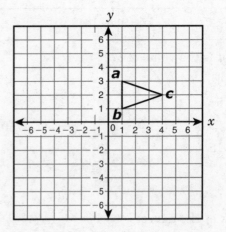

What will the new coordinates of the triangle
be if it is reflected over the y-axis?

   A $a(-1, 3), b(-1, 1), c(-4, 2)$

   B $a(1, -3), b(1, -1), c(4, -2)$

   C $a(-1, -3), b(-1, -1), c(-4, -2)$

   D $a(1, 3), b(1, 1), c(-2, 2)$

9 Use the figure below to answer the question.

Which of the following is a true statement?

   A Angle x is a right angle.

   B Angle x is an obtuse angle.

   C Angle x is an acute angle.

   D Not Here

Jen wants to tile the top of a table that is in the shape of an isosceles right triangle.
The longest side of the table is 36 inches.

Part A   What are the lengths, to the nearest tenth, of the other two sides of the table?
Show your work.

Part B   What is the area, to the nearest tenth, of the table? Show your work.

Part C   The store sells tiles by the box. One box of tiles covers 50 square inches.
How many boxes will Jen need to buy? Explain.

Hiro drew the polygon below.

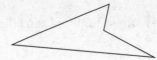

Part A   Will the polygon tessellate? Explain.

Part B   Describe how you would use transformations to create a tessellated plane of Hiro's polygon.

Part C   Use Hiro's figure to create a tessellated design.

The **perimeter** of a closed figure is the distance around the figure. It is measured in linear units. The **area** of a closed figure is the space it covers. It is measured in square units.

To find the perimeter of a triangle or parallelogram, add the lengths of the sides.

The area A of a triangle with base b and height h is $A = \frac{1}{2}bh$.

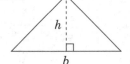

The area A of a parallelogram with base b and height h is $A = bh$.

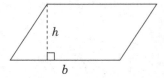

The **Area Addition Postulate** states that the area of a region is equal to the sum of its nonoverlapping parts. So the area of the figure at right is the sum of the area of the shaded parallelogram and the area of the unshaded triangle.

🤚 GUIDED PRACTICE

Problem 1   The area of a rectangle with base b and height h is $A = bh$. Show that a rectangle and a parallelogram with the same base and height have the same area.

Step 1   Cut a right triangle off of the rectangle and translate it to the left to form a parallelogram.

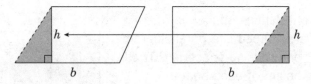

Step 2   By the Area Addition Postulate, the rectangle and the parallelogram have the same area.

Solution   A rectangle with base b and height h has the same area as a parallelogram with base b and height h. The area of each is found using the formula $A = bh$.

ADDITIONAL PROBLEMS

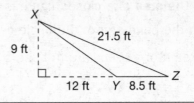

Problem 2 Find the area and perimeter of triangle *XYZ*.

Step 1 Use the Pythagorean Theorem to find *XY*.

$$a^2 + b^2 = c^2$$
$$(9)^2 + (12)^2 = (XY)^2$$
$$81 + 144 = (XY)^2$$
$$225 = (XY)^2$$
$$\sqrt{225} = \sqrt{(XY)^2}$$
$$15 = XY$$

Step 2 Add the lengths of the sides of triangle *XYZ* to find the perimeter.

$$P = 8.5 \text{ ft} + 21.5 \text{ ft} + 15 \text{ ft}$$
$$= 45 \text{ ft}$$

Step 3 Use the formula for the area of a triangle to find the area of triangle *XYZ*.

Solution The perimeter of triangle *XYZ* is 45 ft.

The area of triangle *XYZ* is _____.

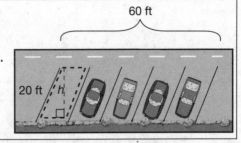

Problem 3 The congruent parking spaces in a parking lot are shaped like parallelograms. The area of one parking space is 207 ft^2. What is the height of each space?

Step 1 Identify the length of the base of one parking space. Because the spaces are congruent, you can divide the total length, 60 ft, by the number of spaces, 5. So, the length of the base of one space is 12 ft.

60 ft ÷ 5 = 12 ft

Step 2 Use the formula for the area of a parallelogram. Substitute the values you know and solve for the height.

Solution The height of each parking space is _____ feet.

⭐ SHORT ANSWER QUESTIONS

Find the perimeter of each figure. Round your answers to the nearest hundredth.

1.

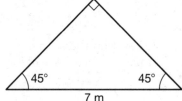

_____

2.

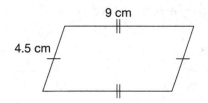

_____

3.

_____

Find the area of each figure. Round your answers to the nearest hundredth.

4.

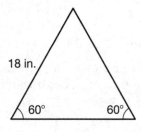

_____

5.

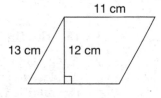

_____

6.

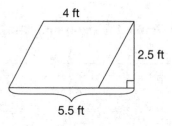

_____

Find the missing measurement.

7. $A = 60$ m^2

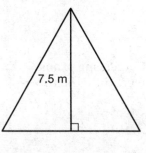

$b =$ _____ m

8. $A = 200$ ft^2

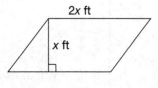

$h =$ _____ ft

9. $A = 60$ mm^2

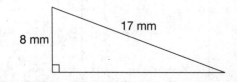

$b =$ _____ mm

Use the diagram at right to solve problems 10 and 11. Round your answers to the nearest hundredth.

10. Find the area of *ABCD*. _____

11. Find the area of triangle *ADE*. _____

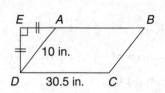

12. The base of a parallelogram is three times the height. The base is 7.5 cm. What is the area of the parallelogram? _____

DIRECTIONS Read each question. Then circle the letter for the correct answer. If a correct answer is <u>not here</u>, circle the letter for "Not Here."

1   A rectangle has a height that is twice its base. A triangle has a base equal to the rectangle's base and a height that is one-half its base. What is the ratio between the area of the rectangle and the area of the triangle?

   A   2:1   **C**   8:1

   B   4:1   **D**   16:1

Use the figure for Problems 2–4.

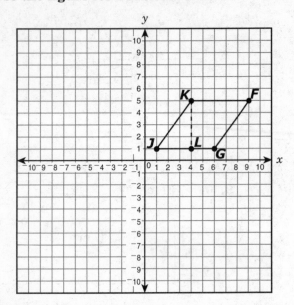

2   What is the perimeter of △*JKL*?

   A   4 units

   B   5 units

   C   12 units

   D   15 units

3   What is the area of parallelogram *JKFG*?

   A   30 square units

   B   25 square units

   C   15 square units

   D   Not Here

4   What is the difference between the area of parallelogram *JKFG* and the perimeter of parallelogram *JKFG*?

   A   0

   B   5

   C   20

   D   40

Use the figure for Problems 5 and 6.

A pig pen, in the shape of a parallelogram, is being divided into three separate enclosed areas by adding two additional fences, *x* and *y*, as shown.

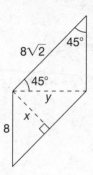

5   How many additional feet of fencing, *x* and *y*, is required to divide the pen into the three separate enclosures?

   A   24.5 ft

   B   13.7 ft

   C   13.3 ft

   D   12 ft

6   What are the areas of the three new enclosures?

   A   24 ft², 24 ft², 48 ft²

   B   16 ft², 16 ft², 32 ft²

   C   18 ft², 18 ft², 36 ft²

   D   Not Here

STAAR PRACTICE: CUMULATIVE

DIRECTIONS Read each question. Then circle the letter for the correct answer.
If a correct answer is <u>not here</u>, circle the letter for "Not Here."

7 What is the midpoint between the points $(-3, \sqrt{7})$ and $(2, 4)$?

A $(-\frac{1}{2}, \frac{4 + \sqrt{7}}{2})$

B $(-\frac{1}{2}, \frac{\sqrt{11}}{2})$

C $(-\frac{5}{2}, \frac{4 - \sqrt{7}}{2})$

D $(-\frac{5}{2}, \frac{\sqrt{11}}{2})$

8 Gene is painting a rectangular mural that measures 16 feet by 24 feet. He divides the rectangle into two congruent triangles and paints one triangle blue and the other triangle red. If he applies two coats of paint to each triangle, how many square feet of blue paint will he use?

A 80 ft^2

B 192 ft^2

C 384 ft^2

D 768 ft^2

9 The slope of a line containing the points $(a, 14)$ and $(2, 5)$ is 9. What is the value of a?

A 3

B 1

C $\frac{2}{9}$

D $\frac{1}{9}$

10 An art building is being built as shown below. Glass windows will be placed on the left and right faces of the building.

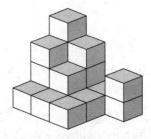

Which of the drawings show the front-left and front-right views of the building?

A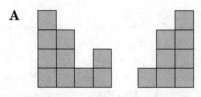

B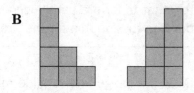

C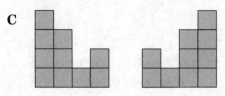

D Not Here

The area of a **trapezoid** with bases b_1 and b_2 is $A = \frac{1}{2} h(b_1 + b_2)$.

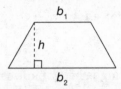

The area of a **rhombus** or **kite** with diagonals d_1 and d_2 is $A = \frac{1}{2}d_1d_2$.

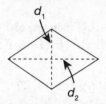
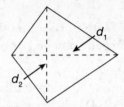

The diagonals of a rhombus are perpendicular and they bisect each other.

The **center** of a regular polygon is equidistant from the vertices of the polygon.

The **apothem** of a regular polygon is a segment drawn perpendicular from the center to a side.

A **central angle** of a regular polygon has its vertex at the center and its sides contain consecutive vertices. The measure of each of the central angles of a regular n-gon is $\frac{360°}{n}$.

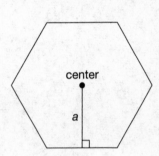

The **area of a regular polygon** with apothem a and perimeter P is $A = \frac{1}{2}aP$.

GUIDED PRACTICE

Problem 1

A glide reflection of the trapezoid at right creates an image that is congruent to the preimage. Fit the preimage and the image together to form a parallelogram and use what you know to develop the formula for the area of a trapezoid.

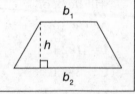

Step 1   Draw the image after a glide reflection of the preimage. Join the two trapezoids to form a parallelogram.

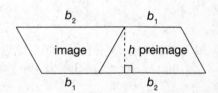

Step 2   By the Area Addition Postulate, the sum of the areas of the two trapezoids is equal to the area of the parallelogram. So the area of one trapezoid is one-half the area of the parallelogram.

$$A = \frac{1}{2} \times (b_1 + b_2) \times h$$

$$= \frac{1}{2}h(b_1 + b_2)$$

Solution   The area of a trapezoid with bases b_1 and b_2 is $A = \frac{1}{2} h(b_1 + b_2)$.

✦ ADDITIONAL PROBLEMS

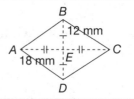

Problem 2 Find the area of rhombus *ABCD*.

Step 1 Find the lengths of the diagonals $\overline{AC}$ and $\overline{BD}$.

$\overline{BE} \cong \overline{ED}$, so $BD = 2(12) = 24$ mm. $A = \frac{1}{2}d_1d_2$
$\overline{AE} \cong \overline{EC}$, so $AC = 2(18) = 36$ mm.

$$= \frac{1}{2}(\underline{\quad})(\underline{\quad}) = \underline{\qquad\qquad}$$

Step 2 Use the formula for the area of a rhombus.
Substitute the lengths of the diagonals into the formula.

Solution The area of rhombus *ABCD* is _____.

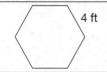

Problem 3 A garden is shaped like a regular hexagon. Each side of the garden is 4 feet long. Find the area of the garden.

Step 1 Add the lengths of the sides to find the perimeter of the garden. Because the polygon is regular, each side is the same length. Multiply the number of sides, 6, by the length of each side, 4 ft.

$$P = 6(4 \text{ ft})$$
$$= 24 \text{ ft}$$

Step 2 Next, find the length of the apothem. The measure of a central angle of a hexagon is $\frac{360°}{6}$ or 60°. The apothem bisects the central angle creating a 30°-60°-90° triangle. The shortest side of the triangle is one-half the side length of the hexagon. Use the 30°–60°–90° Triangle Theorem to find the length of the apothem.

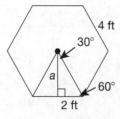

$$a = 2\sqrt{3} \text{ ft}$$

Step 3 Use the formula for the area of a regular polygon to find the area. Round your answer to the nearest hundredth.

$$A = \frac{1}{2}aP$$
$$= \frac{1}{2}(\underline{\qquad\qquad})(\underline{\qquad\qquad})$$
$$= \underline{\qquad\qquad}$$

Step 4 Notice that you can also find the area of the hexagon using the Area Addition Postulate. The central angles of the hexagon divide the hexagon into 6 congruent triangles. Find the area of one triangle and multiply by 6 to find the area of the hexagon.

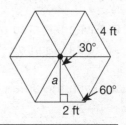

Area of one triangle $= \frac{1}{2}(4 \text{ ft})(2\sqrt{3} \text{ ft})$

Solution The area of the garden is about _____ ft^2.

SHORT ANSWER QUESTIONS

Find the area of each figure. Express the answer in simplified radical form.

1.

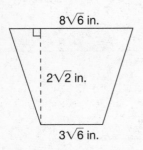

8√6 in.

2√2 in.

3√6 in.

_____

2.

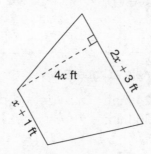

4x ft

2x + 3 ft

x + 1 ft

_____

3.

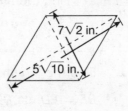

7√2 in.

5√10 in.

_____

4.

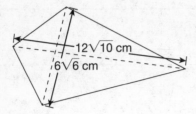

12√10 cm

6√6 cm

_____

5.

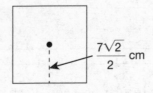

$\frac{7\sqrt{2}}{2}$ cm

_____

6.

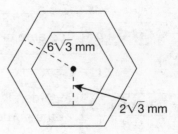

6√3 mm

2√3 mm

_____

Find the perimeter and area. Express the answer in simplified radical form.

7.

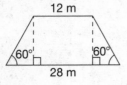

12 m

60°   60°

28 m

P = _____

A = _____

8.

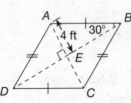

A   B
  4 ft 30°
     E
D   C

P = _____

A = _____

9.

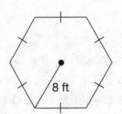

8 ft

P = _____

A = _____

10.

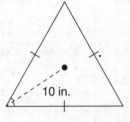

10 in.

P = _____

A = _____

11. Given the area of a rhombus is $A = (8x^2 + 10x)$ cm and the length of $d_1 = 24x$, find the length of d_2.

$d_2 =$

_____

12. Given the area of a rhombus is $A = 14$ m^2 and the length of d_2 is 5 less than 3 times d_1, find d_1 and d_2. $d_1 =$ _____ $d_2 =$ _____

13. Given the area of a rhombus is $A = 52\sqrt{6}$ in.^{2} and the length of $d_1 = 4\sqrt{3}$, find the length of d_2.

$d_2 =$ _____

14. Given a square with a radius of 6 cm, find the area of the square. $A =$ _____

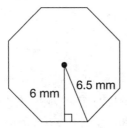 STAAR PRACTICE

DIRECTIONS Read each question. Then circle the letter for the correct answer. If a correct answer is <u>not here</u>, circle the letter for "Not Here."

1 A regular octagon with apothem of 6 mm and a radius of 6.5 mm is shown in the figure.

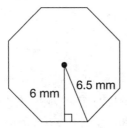

What is the perimeter of the octagon?

A 20 mm^2 **C** 40 mm^2

B 25 mm^2 **D** 48 mm^2

2 A regular hexagon with apothem of $\sqrt{3}$ inches and a radius of 2 inches is shown in the figure.

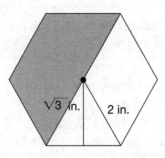

What is the area of the shaded trapezoid?

A $3\sqrt{6}$ in.^{2} **C** $2\sqrt{3}$ in.^{2}

B $3\sqrt{3}$ in.^{2} **D** $\sqrt{3}$ in.^{2}

3 What is the perimeter of a square with a diagonal of $x\sqrt{2}$?

A $4x\sqrt{2}$ **C** $2x$

B x^2 **D** $4x$

4 Fabric for a lampshade pattern is cut out in the shape of a regular trapezoid.

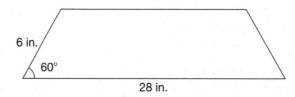

What is the area of the lampshade fabric?

A 168 in.^{2}

B 145.5 in.^{2}

C 129.9 in.^{2}

D 72.75 in.^{2}

5 Look at the figure of a baseball field.

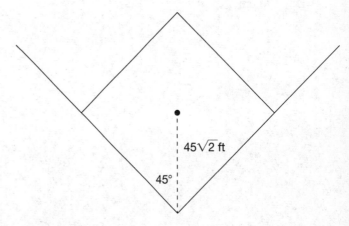

What is the area inside the baseball diamond?

A 127 ft^2

B 255 ft^2

C 2025 ft^2

D 8100 ft^2

⭐ STAAR PRACTICE: CUMULATIVE

DIRECTIONS Read each question. Then circle the letter for the correct answer.
If a correct answer is <u>not here</u>, circle the letter for "Not Here."

6 Which of the following lines is perpendicular to
$y + 1 = \frac{2}{3}(x - 5)$?

A $3y = 2x - 15$

B $y + 7 = \frac{3}{2}(x + 4)$

C $y = \frac{2}{3x} + 1$

D $2y = -3x - 11$

7 An art student is creating a design using
triangles that are balanced using side lengths
that are Pythagorean triples. Which length
represents the hypotenuse of a triangle with
leg lengths of 9 cm and 40 cm?

A   10 cm

B   41 cm

C   49 cm

D   100 cm

8 Consider the validity of the following
conditional statement.

> If a polygon has four sides, then it is
> a quadrilateral.

Is this a valid statement? Why or Why not?

A   Yes, all quadrilaterals have four sides.

B   Yes, all polygons are quadrilaterals.

C   No, the four sided polygon could be
a rhombus.

D   No, the quadrilateral could be
a parallelogram.

9 Matt has made the following conditional
statement.

> If it is Saturday, then there is no
> football practice.

Which of the following is a possible
counterexample to the converse of
Matt's statement?

A   A special game may be scheduled
for Saturday.

B   There is no football practice on Monday.

C   There is not a football game on Saturday.

D   Not Here

Lesson 20   Circumference and Area of Circles

The **circumference** of a circle is the distance around the circle.
The circumference of a circle with radius r is $C = 2\pi r$ or $C = \pi d$.

To develop the formula for the area of a circle, divide a circle into congruent
pieces and arrange the pieces to form a figure that looks like a parallelogram.
The base of the figure is one-half the circumference of the circle, πr, and the
height of the figure is r.

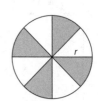

Using the formula for the area of a parallelogram, the area is $\pi r \times r$ or πr^2.

The area of a circle with radius r is $A = \pi r^2$.

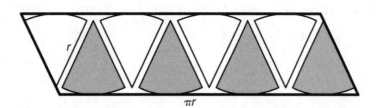

 GUIDED PRACTICE

· ·

Problem 1

Find the circumference and area of the circle.
Round your answer to the nearest hundredth.

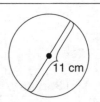

11 cm

Step 1   Use the formula for the circumference of a circle.
The diameter d is 11 cm.

$C = \pi d$
$\quad = \pi(11 \text{ cm})$
$\quad \approx 34.56 \text{ cm}$

Step 2   Find the radius of the circle. The radius is one-half the diameter.

$r = \frac{1}{2}(11 \text{ cm})$
$\quad = 5.5 \text{ cm}$

Step 3   Use the formula for the area of a circle. The radius is 5.5 cm.

$A = \pi r^2$
$\quad = \pi(5.5 \text{ cm})^2$
$\quad = \pi(30.25 \text{ cm}^2)$
$\quad \approx 95.03 \text{ cm}^2$

Solution

The circumference of the circle is about 34.56 cm.
The area of the circle is about 95.03 cm².

★ ADDITIONAL PROBLEMS

Problem 2 The area of a circle is 700 m². What is the radius and circumference of the circle?

Step 1 The area of the circle is given. Substitute the area into the formula for the area of a circle and solve for r.

$$A = \pi r^2$$
$$700 \text{ m}^2 = \pi r^2$$
$$\frac{700}{\pi} \text{ m}^2 = r^2$$
$$15 \text{ m} \approx r$$

Step 2 Substitute the value for r into the formula for the circumference of a circle.

$$C = 2\pi r$$
$$= 2\pi(\underline{\hspace{2cm}}) \text{ m}$$
$$\approx \underline{\hspace{2cm}} \text{ m}$$

Solution The radius of the circle is about 15 m.
The circumference of the circle is about _____ m.

Problem 3 The circular base of a flagpole is surrounded by a circular walkway. The walkway is the shaded region in the figure at right. Find the area of the walkway. Round your answer to the nearest whole number.

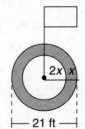

Step 1 Find the value of x. The diameter of the larger circle can be represented by the expression $2x + x + 2x + x = 6x$. The diameter of the larger circle is 21 ft, so set the two expressions equal and solve for x.

$$6x = 21 \text{ ft}$$
$$x = 3.5 \text{ ft}$$

Step 2 Now, find the radius of the larger circle and the radius of the smaller circle. The radius of the larger circle is $3x$ and the radius of the smaller circle is $2x$. Substitute the value for x to find each radius.

Larger: $3x = 3(3.5) = 10.5$ ft

Smaller: $2x = 2(3.5) = 7$ ft

Step 3 Use the formula for the area of a circle to find each area. Then subtract the areas. Round your answer to the nearest whole number.

Solution The area of the walkway is about _____ ft².

     Measuring Up® to the Geometry End-of-Course Exam

★ SHORT ANSWER QUESTIONS

Find the circumference and area of each circle. Round your answers to the nearest hundredth.

1. $d = 13$ cm

C = _____ cm

A = _____ cm²

2. $r = \sqrt{5}$ in.

C = _____ in.

A = _____ in.²

3. $d = \frac{2}{3}$ ft

C = _____ ft

A = _____ ft²

4. $r = 4\sqrt{3}$ mm

C = _____ mm

A = _____ mm²

5. $d = 6.48$ ft

C = _____ ft

A = _____ ft²

6. $r = 3\pi$ m

C = _____ m

A = _____ m²

Find each measurement. Express your answer in simplified radical form. Leave π in your answer.

7. $r = 3x + 1$ in.

C = _____ in.

A = _____ in.²

8. $C = 20\pi\sqrt{2}$ ft

A = _____ ft²

9. $A = 500\pi$ ft

C = _____ ft²

10. $d = 8\pi\sqrt{2}$ in. C = _____ in.

A = _____ in.²

11. The rim diameter of a bicycle wheel is approximately 622 mm. Find the circumference of the wheel to the nearest hundredth. C = _____ mm.

12. The area of one circle is the same as 4 times the circumference of another circle. What is the radius? r = _____

13. Circle A has a circumference of $6\pi\sqrt{2}$ and Circle B has a circumference of $4\pi\sqrt{6}$. Which circle has the larger area? _____

14. Two circles have the same center. The circumference of the small circle is 6π inches and the circumference of the large circle is 10π inches. Leave π in your answers.

a. Find the areas of the small and large circles. A = _____ in.²

A = _____ in.²

b. Find the area of the shaded region. A = _____ in.²

🟦 STAAR PRACTICE

DIRECTIONS Read each question. Then circle the letter for the correct answer. If a correct answer is <u>not here</u>, circle the letter for "Not Here."

1 A circle is inscribed in a square with a side length 10.

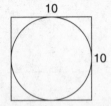

What is the area of the circle?

A 10π **C** 100π

B 25π **D** Not Here

2 The world's largest cookie, with a diameter of approximately 31 meters, weighed an astonishing 40,000 pounds. What was the approximate area of the top of the cookie?

A 49 m^2 **C** 755 m^2

B 97 m^2 **D** 3019 m^2

3 A nut with an inner circumference of 3π inches is shown in the figure.

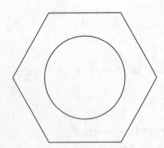

What is the area of the tip of the bolt that will fit the nut?

A $\frac{9}{4}\pi \text{ in.}^2$

B $7\pi \text{ in.}^2$

C $9\pi \text{ in.}^2$

D Not Here

4 An hour hand of a clock is 7 inches long. Approximately how far does the endpoint of the hour hand travel in one hour?

A 14 in.   **C** 44 in.

B 22 in.   **D** 154 in.

5 A watermelon with a 112 cm girth is cut in half. What is the area of the circular cross section?

A 112 cm^2 **C** 998 cm^2

B 318 cm^2 **D** Not Here

6 A baker is piping decorative icing around the circumference of a round cake. The area of the cake's top is $64\pi \text{ in.}^2$.

If the baker can pipe $\frac{1}{2}$ inch of icing per second, how many seconds will it take to add a decorative trim of icing around the edge of the cake? Round your answer to the nearest whole number.

Record your answer in the boxes below. Then fill in the bubbles. Be sure to use the correct place value.

★ STAAR PRACTICE: CUMULATIVE

DIRECTIONS Read each question. Then circle the letter for the correct answer. If a correct answer is <u>not here,</u> circle the letter for "Not Here."

7 A right rectangular pyramid is intersected by a plane as shown in the figure.

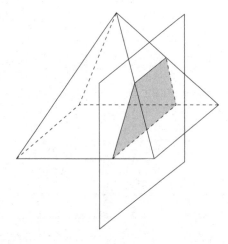

Which shape represents the intersection of the rectangular pyramid and the plane?

A Rectangle

B Square

C Trapezoid

D Triangle

8 The net diagram of a 3-D shape is shown in the figure.

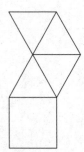

Which of the following describes the 3-D shape?

A Square pyramid

B Triangular pyramid

C Triangular prism

D Cone

9 Line segment *GK* consists of the endpoints *G*(–2, –3) and *K*(6, 6).

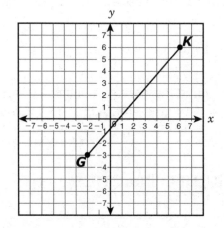

What is the length of $\overline{GK}$?

A $\sqrt{12}$ **C** $\sqrt{145}$

B $\sqrt{17}$ **D** $\sqrt{172}$

10 A rectangular field measures 150 meters by 60 meters. A fence surrounds the entire field with posts in each corner.

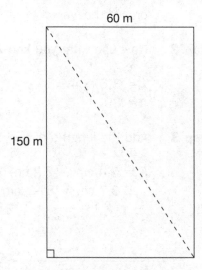

What is the distance between the two non-adjacent fence posts?

A 156 m   **C** 210 m

B 161.6 m   **D** 4500 m

A **composite figure** is made up of simple shapes such as triangles, parallelograms, trapezoids, and circles. The composite figure at right can be divided into a triangle, a square, and a rectangle.

To find the perimeter of a composite figure, use what you know about the simple shapes to find the length of each side of the figure.

To find the area of a composite figure, find the area of each simple shape and use the Area Addition Postulate.

🔷 GUIDED PRACTICE

Problem 1   Find the perimeter of the composite figure.

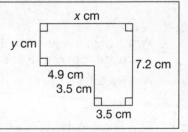

Step 1   Divide the figure into simpler shapes. There are two ways to divide the figure into a rectangle and a square. Choose one of the ways.

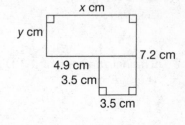

Step 2   Now use what you know to find the values of x and y.

$x = 3.5 + 4.9$ $y = 7.2 - 3.5$
   $= 8.4$ $= 3.7$

Step 3   Add the lengths of the sides to find the perimeter.

$P = 8.4$ cm $+ 7.2$ cm $+ 3.5$ cm $+ 3.5$ cm $+ 4.9$ cm
    $+ 3.7$ cm $= 31.2$ cm

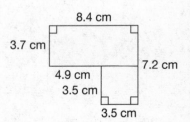

Solution   The perimeter of the composite figure is 31.2 cm.

![Texas icon] **ADDITIONAL PROBLEMS**

Problem 2 Find the area of the composite figure.

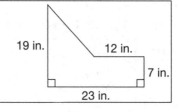

Step 1 Divide the figure into a right triangle and a rectangle.

Step 2 Find the base and height of the triangle.

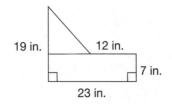

height of triangle = 19 in. − 7 in. = 12 in.
base of triangle = 23 in. − 12 in. = 11 in.

Step 3 Find the areas of the triangle and rectangle.

$$A = \tfrac{1}{2}bh$$

$$= \tfrac{1}{2}(\underline{\hspace{1cm}} \text{ in.})(\underline{\hspace{1cm}} \text{ in.})$$

$$= \underline{\hspace{1cm}} \text{ square inches}$$

$$A = bh$$

$$= (\underline{\hspace{1cm}} \text{ in.})(\underline{\hspace{1cm}} \text{ in.})$$

$$= \underline{\hspace{1cm}} \text{ in.}^2$$

Step 4 Add the areas of the triangle and rectangle.

Solution The area of the composite figure is _____ square inches.

Problem 3 A rectangular pond is surrounded on three sides by a garden. Find the area of the garden.

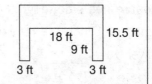

Step 1 Divide the figure into 3 rectangles and use what you know to find the lengths of all the sides.

Step 2 Find the area of each rectangle using the formula $A = bh$. Then add the areas to find the area of the composite figure.

Step 3 Now find the area of the entire region and the area of the pond.

Length of entire region: 3 ft + 18 ft + 3 ft = 24 ft

Area of entire region: $A = (\underline{\hspace{1cm}} \text{ ft})(\underline{\hspace{1cm}} \text{ ft}) = \underline{\hspace{1cm}} \text{ ft}^2$

Area of pond: $A = (\underline{\hspace{1cm}} \text{ ft})(\underline{\hspace{1cm}} \text{ ft}) = \underline{\hspace{1cm}} \text{ ft}^2$

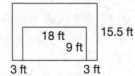

Step 4 Subtract the area of the pond from the area of the entire region.

Solution The area of the garden is _____ ft^2.

◆ SHORT ANSWER QUESTIONS

Find the perimeter and area of each composite figure. Round to the nearest hundredth.

1.

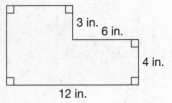

2.

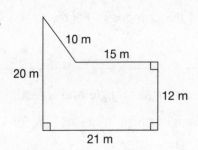

3.

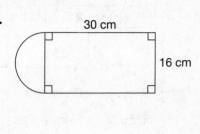

$P =$ _____ $A =$ _____ $P =$ _____ $A =$ _____ $P =$ _____ $A =$ _____

4. A rectangle has a length of 12 inches and a width of 10 inches. A semicircle sits on top with a diameter that is the same as the width of the rectangle. Find the distance around the shape. Leave π in your answer. $A =$ _____

5. A rectangle with a length of 12 meters and a width of 6 meters has a square with side lengths of 3 meters removed from the interior. What is the remaining area of the figure? $A =$ _____

6. Two circles have the same center. The radius of the larger circle is $10\sqrt{2}$ meters and the radius of the smaller circle is $3\sqrt{2}$ meters. If the small circle is removed, what is the remaining area of the figure? Leave π in your answer. $A =$ _____

7. A square has side lengths of 8 inches. A circle with a diameter of 4 inches and another square with side lengths of 1 inch are removed from the interior. What is the remaining area of the figure? Leave π in your answer. $A =$ _____

8. Ben wants to put a fence around the garden shown below.

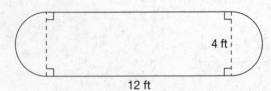

How much fencing, rounded to the nearest foot, will he need? If fencing costs $10.35 a foot, how much will it cost to fence the garden? _____ _____

9. Refer to Problem 8. Ben wants to lay mulch in the garden. How much area, rounded to the nearest foot, will he need to mulch? One bag of mulch covers 11 square feet. How many bags of mulch will he need?

_____ _____

STAAR PRACTICE

DIRECTIONS Read each question. Then circle the letter for the correct answer.
If a correct answer is <u>not here</u>, circle the letter for "Not Here."

1 A handheld gaming device has a rectangular face 12 cm wide and 7 cm tall. The screen of the device is shown inside the rectangle below.

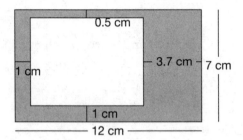

What is the area of the shaded region that surrounds the screen of the device?

A 40.15 cm²

B 43.85 cm²

C 78.45 cm²

D 84 cm²

2 A semi-circular arch window is placed on the top of a rectangle to form a window as shown in the figure.

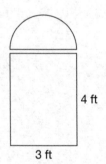

What is the total perimeter of the window?

A 7 ft

B 14 ft

C 15.7 ft

D 20.4 ft

3 A boat dock is shown in the figure.

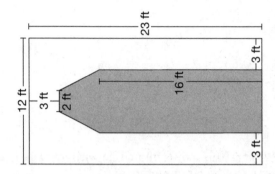

What is the area of the dock?

A 276 ft²   **C** 156 ft²

B 164 ft²   **D** 138 ft²

4 A composite figure with an area of 75 square units is shown in the figure.

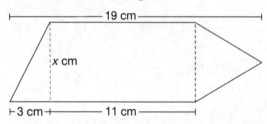

What is the value of x?

A 5   **C** 10

B 7   **D** 15

5 A composite figure is formed from an equilateral triangle sitting on top of a square. The side lengths of the triangle and square are congruent. If the perimeter of the figure is 100 cm, what is the length of one side of the figure?

A 25 cm   **C** 10 cm

B 20 cm   **D** Not Here

⬣ STAAR PRACTICE: CUMULATIVE

DIRECTIONS Read each question. Then circle the letter for the correct answer. If a correct answer is <u>not here</u>, circle the letter for "Not Here."

6 What is the length of the hypotenuse of a right triangle with legs of length 4 and 9?

   A $\sqrt{5}$

   B $\sqrt{13}$

   C $\sqrt{65}$

   D $\sqrt{97}$

7 What is the radius of a circle with an area that is twice the circumference?

   A 1

   B 2

   C 4

   D Not Here

8 Consider the statement.

> If two triangles are congruent, then they are similar.

Which of the following is true when applied to the statement?

   A Inverse

   B Converse

   C Contrapositive

   D Not here

9 What is the slope of the line passing through the points $(1, 4)$ and $(3, -4)$?

   A Undefined

   B -4

   C 0

   D $\frac{1}{4}$

     Measuring Up® to the Geometry End-of-Course Exam

A **prism** is a polyhedron with two parallel congruent bases which are polygons. The bases are connected by lateral faces which are parallelograms.

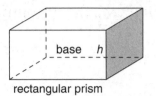

rectangular prism

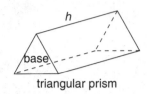

triangular prism

- The **lateral area** L of a right prism with base perimeter P and height h is $L = Ph$.

- The **surface area** S of a right prism with lateral area L and base area B is $S = L + 2B$.

- The **volume** V of a prism with height h and base area B is $V = Bh$.

A **pyramid** is a polyhedron with a base that is a polygon and triangular lateral faces that meet at a common point called the **vertex**.

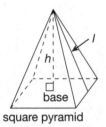

- The **lateral area** L of a regular pyramid with slant height l and base perimeter P is $L = \frac{1}{2}Pl$.

- The **surface area** S of a regular pyramid with slant height l, base perimeter P, and base area B is $S = \frac{1}{2}Pl + B$.

square pyramid

- The **volume** V of a pyramid with height h and base area B is $V = \frac{1}{3}Bh$.

★ GUIDED PRACTICE

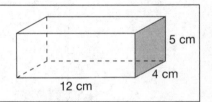

5 cm
4 cm
12 cm

Problem 1 Find the surface area of the prism.

Step 1 Find the perimeter of the base. The base is a rectangle with length 12 cm and width 4 cm. Use the formula for finding the perimeter of a rectangle.

$P = 2l + 2w$
$= 2(12 \text{ cm}) + 2(4 \text{ cm})$
$= 24 \text{ cm} + 8 \text{ cm}$
$= 32 \text{ cm}$

Step 2 Find the lateral area of the prism. The prism has a height of 5 cm.

$L = Ph$
$= (32 \text{ cm})(5 \text{ cm})$
$= 160 \text{ cm}^2$

Step 3 Find the area of the base. Use the formula for finding the area of a rectangle.

$A = lw$
$= (12 \text{ cm})(4 \text{ cm})$
$= 48 \text{ cm}^2$

Step 4 Find the surface area of the prism.

$S = L + 2B$
$= 160 \text{ cm}^2 + 2(48 \text{ cm}^2)$
$= 160 \text{ cm}^2 + 96 \text{ cm}^2$
$= 256 \text{ cm}^2$

Solution The surface area of the prism is 256 cm².

★ ADDITIONAL PROBLEMS

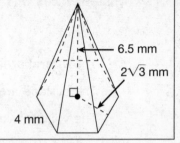

Problem 2   Find the volume of the regular hexagonal pyramid. Round to the nearest tenth.

Step 1   The base of the pyramid is a regular hexagon. Find the area of a hexagon with apothem $2\sqrt{3}$ mm. The side length is 4 mm, so the perimeter of the base is 6(4 mm) or 24 mm.

$$A = \tfrac{1}{2}\,aP$$
$$= \tfrac{1}{2}\,(2\sqrt{3}\ \text{mm})(24\ \text{mm})$$
$$= 24\sqrt{3}\ \text{mm}^2$$

Step 2   Find the volume of the pyramid. The height of the pyramid is 6.5 mm.

$$V = \tfrac{1}{3}\,Bh$$
$$= \tfrac{1}{3}\,(\underline{\hspace{1cm}}\ \text{mm})\,(\underline{\hspace{0.6cm}}\ \text{mm})$$
$$\approx \underline{\hspace{1cm}}\ \text{mm}^3$$

Solution   The volume of the pyramid is about \underline{\hspace{3cm}}.

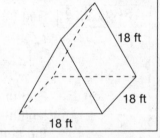

Problem 3   Sara is building a glass greenhouse. How much glass does she need for the greenhouse?

Step 1   Find the perimeter of a base. Each base is an equilateral triangle with side lengths of 18 ft.

$$P = 3(18\ \text{ft})$$
$$= 54\ \text{ft}$$

Step 2   Next, find the lateral area of the greenhouse. The height is 18 feet. (Remember the prism is on its side.)

Step 3   Determine the area of a base. Because the triangle is equilateral, the altitude is the longer leg of a 30°-60°-90° right triangle. The shorter leg of the triangle is 9 ft, so the longer leg is $9\sqrt{3}$. Find the area of the base using the formula for the area of a triangle.

$$A = \tfrac{1}{2}bh$$
$$= \tfrac{1}{2}\,(\underline{\hspace{1.5cm}}\text{ft})\,(\underline{\hspace{1.5cm}}\text{ft})$$
$$= \underline{\hspace{1.5cm}}\ \text{ft}^2$$

Step 4   Find the surface area of the greenhouse.

Step 5   Find the area of the lateral face that is the floor and subtract it from the surface area.

Solution   Sara needs about \underline{\hspace{1.5cm}} ft² of glass.

SHORT ANSWER QUESTIONS

Find the lateral area and surface area. Round to the nearest hundredth.

1.

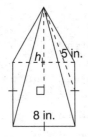

LA = _____

SA = _____

2.

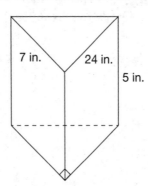

LA = _____

SA = _____

3.

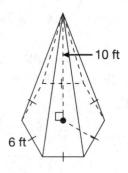

LA = _____

SA = _____

For Questions 4–6, find the volume. Round to the nearest tenth.

4.

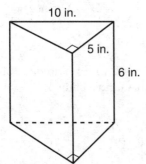

V = _____

5.

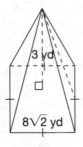

V = _____

6.

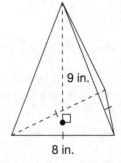

V = _____

7.

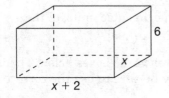

SA = 88   x = _____

8. Manuel is eating a stack of waffles that are 8 inches square. If the height of the stack is 4 inches, what is the volume of the waffles? V = _____

9. A tent is constructed with a regular decagon floor that has sides of 5 feet. The height of the tent is 12 feet and the apothem of the floor is $8\sqrt{3}$ feet. What is the volume of the tent? Express your answer in simplified radical form. V = _____

10. The volume of a cube with side length x is equal to the volume of a square pyramid with a side length of 6 inches and a height of 9 inches. Find the side length of the cube. Express your answer in simplified radical form. x = _____

STAAR PRACTICE

DIRECTIONS Read each question. Then circle the letter for the correct answer. If a correct answer is <u>not here</u>, circle the letter for "Not Here."

1 The volume of the prism below is 252π square units. The diameter of the base is 12 units.

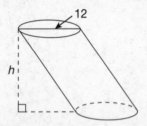

What is the height of the prism?

A 1.75 units   **C** 7 units

B 6 units   **D** 42 units

Use the figure for Questions 2 and 3.

The net of a right equilateral pyramid with side lengths of $4\sqrt{3}$ feet is shown in the figure.

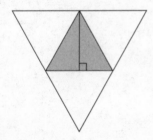

2 The pyramid has a height of $3\sqrt{3}$ ft. What is the volume of the pyramid represented by the net?

A 36 ft^3 **C** 52 ft^3

B 48 ft^3 **D** 64 ft^3

3 What is the surface area of the pyramid represented by the net?

A $4\sqrt{3} \text{ ft}^2$ **C** $36\sqrt{3} \text{ ft}^2$

B $12\sqrt{3} \text{ ft}^2$ **D** $48\sqrt{3} \text{ ft}^2$

4 A company is designing a container for its product and has narrowed it down to the shapes below. The volumes of the containers are equal.

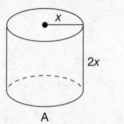 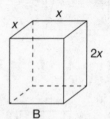

Which should the company choose in order to use the least amount of material?

A B, since $1 < \pi$ **C** A, since $1 < \pi$

B B, since $\pi < 1$ **D** A, since $\pi < 1$

5 A prism has a height of 2 units. The base of the prism is the composite figure shown.

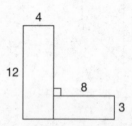

What is the volume, in cubic units, of the composite prism?

Record your answer in the boxes below. Then fill in the bubbles. Be sure to use the correct place value.

STAAR PRACTICE: CUMULATIVE

DIRECTIONS Read each question. Then circle the letter for the correct answer.
If a correct answer is <u>not here</u>, circle the letter for "Not Here."

6 What is the length of a diagonal of a square with side lengths of 10 cm?

   A $2\sqrt{5}$ cm

   B $5\sqrt{2}$ cm

   C $10\sqrt{2}$ cm

   D $20\sqrt{2}$ cm

7 A wallpaper design is made up of only one geometric shape. There are no gaps between each pattern shape. Which of the following shapes could not be used to create the wallpaper design?

   A Square

   B Hexagon

   C Triangle

   D Octagon

8 A right triangle has side lengths of 8 mm and 15 mm. What is the length of the hypotenuse?

   A $\sqrt{23}$ mm

   B 17 mm

   C $\sqrt{161}$ mm

   D 289 mm

9 What is the slope of the line perpendicular to $y - 2 = 3(x + 1)$?

   A -2

   B $-\frac{1}{3}$

   C 1

   D 3

A **cylinder** is a solid with two parallel bases which are circles. The bases are connected by a curved lateral surface.

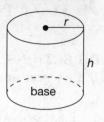

- The **lateral area** L of a right cylinder with radius r and height h is $L = 2\pi rh$.

- The **surface area** S of a right cylinder with lateral area L and base area B is $S = L + 2B$.

- The **volume** V of a cylinder with height h and base area B is $V = Bh$.

A **cone** is a solid with a base that is a circle and a curved lateral surface that connects the base to a common point called the **vertex**.

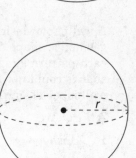

- The **lateral area** L of a right cone with slant height l and radius r is $L = \pi rl$.

- The **surface area** S of a right cone with slant height l, radius r, and base area B is $S = L + B$.

- The **volume** V of a cone with height h and base area B is $V = \frac{1}{3}Bh$.

A **sphere** is the set of all points in space that are a given distance from a point called the **center** of the sphere.

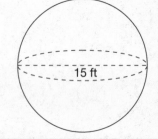

- The **surface area** S of a sphere with radius r is $S = 4\pi r^2$.

- The **volume** V of a sphere with radius r is $V = \frac{4}{3}\pi r^3$.

✦ GUIDED PRACTICE

| **Problem 1** | Find the volume of the sphere. Round to the nearest hundredth. |

15 ft

| **Step 1** | Divide the diameter of the sphere by 2 to find the radius. |

$$r = \frac{1}{2}d$$
$$= \frac{1}{2}\,(15 \text{ ft})$$
$$= 7.5 \text{ ft}$$

| **Step 2** | Use the formula for the volume of a sphere. Substitute the value for r found in Step 1. |

$$V = \frac{4}{3}\pi r^3$$
$$= \frac{4}{3}\pi\,(7.5 \text{ ft})^3$$
$$\approx 1767.15 \text{ ft}^3$$

| **Solution** | The volume of the sphere is about 1767.15 ft³. |

★ ADDITIONAL PROBLEMS

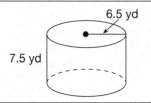

6.5 yd

7.5 yd

Problem 2 Find the surface area of the cylinder. Round to the nearest hundredth.

Step 1 Find the lateral area of the cylinder. The cylinder has a radius of 6.5 yd and a height of 7.5 yd.

$L = 2\pi rh$
$= 2\pi(6.5 \text{ yd})(7.5 \text{ yd})$
$\approx 306.31 \text{ yd}^2$

Step 2 To use the formula for surface area of a cylinder, you need to first find the area of the base. The base is a circle. Use the formula for the area of a circle.

$A = \pi r^2$
$= \pi(\underline{\hspace{2cm}} \text{ yd})^2$
$\approx \underline{\hspace{2cm}} \text{ yd}^2$

Step 3 Use the formula for the surface area of a cylinder.

$S = L + 2B$
$= \underline{\hspace{2cm}} \text{ yd}^2 + 2(\underline{\hspace{2cm}}) \text{ yd}^2$
$= \underline{\hspace{2cm}} \text{ yd}^2$

Solution The surface area of the cylinder is about \underline{\hspace{2cm}} yd^2.

Problem 3 Lisa is making party hats shaped like cones. How much paper does she need for twenty party hats?

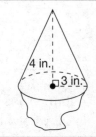

4 in.

3 in.

Step 1 First you need to find the slant height. The height of the hat is 4 inches and the radius of the base is 3 inches. The height, radius, and slant height form a right triangle. Use the Pythagorean Theorem to find the slant height.

$a^2 + b^2 = c^2$
$(\underline{\hspace{0.6cm}})^2 + (\underline{\hspace{0.6cm}})^2 = l^2$
$\underline{\hspace{0.6cm}} + \underline{\hspace{0.6cm}} = l^2$
$\underline{\hspace{1.2cm}} = l$
$\underline{\hspace{0.6cm}} = l$

Step 2 Now use the formula for the lateral area of a cone.

Step 3 Multiply the lateral area by 20 to find the amount of paper needed. Round your answer up to the nearest whole number.

Solution Lisa needs \underline{\hspace{2cm}} ft^2 of paper to make the hats.

★ SHORT ANSWER QUESTIONS

Find the volume and surface area. Round to the nearest hundredth.

1. Cylinder $r = 3$ in. $h = 5$ in.

SA = _____

V = _____

2. Cylinder $d = 18$ ft $h = 2$ ft

SA = _____

V = _____

3. Cone $r = 3$ cm $h = 4$ cm

SA = _____

V = _____

4. Cone $d = 8$ in. $h = 6$ in.

SA = _____

V = _____

5. Sphere $r = 10$ ft

SA = _____

V = _____

6. Sphere $d = 2\sqrt{5}$ mm

SA = _____

V = _____

Find the volume and/or surface area. Leave π and simplified radicals in your answer.

7. Sphere SA = $1{,}024\pi$ mm^2

V = _____

8. Cylinder $r = 3\sqrt{2}$ in. $h = 2\sqrt{6}$ in.

SA = _____

V = _____

9. Cone $d = 8\sqrt{3}$ cm $h = 8$ cm

SA = _____

V = _____

10. Cylinder $h = 2\sqrt{2}$ cm $d = 3\sqrt{5}$ cm

SA = _____

11. A farm silo is shaped according to the diagram shown. The diameter of the cylinder is 22 yd and the overall height of the silo is 10 yd. The height of the cylinder is 4 yd. What is the volume of the silo? Leave π in your answer. V = _____

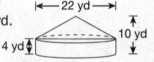

12. A cone has a height that is 4 times the radius. If the volume of the cone is 288π, what is the length of the radius and the height? r = _____ h = _____

13. Will a sphere with a volume of 100π in.^{3} fit inside a cylinder with a height of 10 in. and a volume of 125π in.^{3}? Why or why not? Find each diameter to the nearest hundredth to answer the question.

_____

_____

14. The planetarium has a spherical garden that needs painting on the outside. The diameter of the sphere is 16 ft. Find the surface area of the sphere to the nearest whole number. SA = _____

15. Find the radius and the height of a cylinder with a surface area of 96π ft^2 and a height that is 4 feet more than the radius. r = _____ h = _____

STAAR PRACTICE

DIRECTIONS Read each question. Then circle the letter for the correct answer.
If a correct answer is <u>not here</u>, circle the letter for "Not Here."

1 A right circular cylinder and a right cone have the same radius and height. What is the ratio of the volume of the cylinder to the volume of the cone?

  A $1:1$

  B $1:3$

  C $3:1$

  D $\frac{1}{3}:1$

2 A right cylinder is shown in the figure.

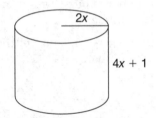

Which expression represents the volume of the cylinder?

  A $16\pi x^3 + 4\pi x^2$

  B $8\pi x^3 + 2\pi x^2$

  C $16\pi x^2 + 4\pi x$

  D $8\pi x^2 + 2\pi x$

3 A right cone with a 45° base angle and slant length of $3\sqrt{2}$ is shown in the figure.

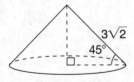

What is the volume of the cone?

  A $6\pi\sqrt{2}$ cubic units

  B $9\pi\sqrt{2}$ cubic units

  C 9π cubic units

  D 27π cubic units

4 A snowball melts at a rate proportional to its surface area. What is the volume of a spherical snowball when its circumference is 8π in.?

  A   85 in.^{3}

  B   67 in.^{3}

  C   268 in.^{3}

  D   2145 in.^{3}

5 How much aluminum does it take to create a cylindrical aluminum can with a 6 cm diameter and 17 cm height?

  A   153 cm^2

  B   377 cm^2

  C   612 cm^2

  D   1923 cm^2

6 What happens to the volume of a sphere when the radius is doubled?

  A   The volume is cubed.

  B   The volume is doubled.

  C   The volume is increased by four.

  D   The volume is eight times as great.

7 Find the volume of a cone with a base diameter of 2 and a height that is four times the radius. Round to the nearest tenth.

Record your answer in the boxes below. Then fill in the bubbles. Be sure to use the correct place value.

⬥ STAAR PRACTICE: CUMULATIVE

DIRECTIONS Read each question. Then circle the letter for the correct answer. If a correct answer is <u>not here</u>, circle the letter for "Not Here."

8 What is the perimeter of a right triangle with area of 30 and a base of 5?

   A 12 units

   B 13 units

   C 17 units

   D 30 units

9 Find the slope of the line perpendicular to the line passing through the points (2, 1) and (4, −4).

   A 2

   B $\frac{2}{5}$

   C $-\frac{1}{2}$

   D $-\frac{5}{2}$

10 Look at the pattern below.

> 1, 3, 9, 27, 81

Which statement describes the pattern?

   A Each number is three more than the previous number.

   B Each number is three times the previous number.

   C Each number is one-third of the previous number.

   D Each number is one-sixth of the previous number.

11 What is the area of a circle with circumference 2π?

   A π square units

   B 2π square units

   C 4π square units

   D 16π square units

A **composite solid** is made up of simple solids such as prisms, pyramids, cylinders, cones, and spheres. The composite solid at right can be divided into a triangular prism and a rectangular prism.

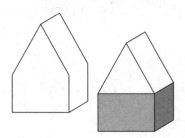

To find the surface area of a composite solid, add the surface areas of each simple solid.

To find the volume of a composite solid, add the volumes of each simple solid.

GUIDED PRACTICE

. . . .

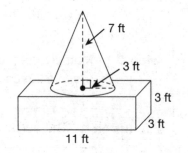

Problem 1 Find the volume of the composite solid.

Step 1	Find the base area of the prism. The base is a rectangle 11 ft long and 3 ft wide.	$A = lw$ $= (11 \text{ ft}) (3 \text{ ft})$ $= 33 \text{ ft}^2$
Step 2	Find the volume of the prism. The prism is 3 ft high.	$V = Bh$ $= (33 \text{ ft}^2) (3 \text{ ft})$ $= 99 \text{ ft}^3$
Step 3	The base of the cone has a radius of 3 ft. Determine the area of the circle.	$A = \pi r^2$ $= \pi (3 \text{ ft})^2$ $= 9\pi \text{ ft}^2$ $\approx 28.27 \text{ ft}^2$
Step 4	Next, find the volume of the cone. The cone has a height of 7 ft.	$V = \frac{1}{3}Bh$ $= \frac{1}{3}(28.27 \text{ ft}^2) (7 \text{ ft})$ $= 65.96 \text{ ft}^3$
Step 5	Now add the volumes of the rectangular prism and the cone. $99 \text{ ft}^3 + 65.96 \text{ ft}^3 = 164.96 \text{ ft}^3$	

Solution The volume of the composite solid is about 164.96 ft^3.

🔺 **ADDITIONAL PROBLEMS**

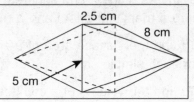

Problem 2 Find the surface area of the composite solid.

Step 1 Find the perimeter of the base. Use the formula for the perimeter of a rectangle.

$P = 2l + 2w$

$= 2(\underline{\hspace{1cm}}$ cm$) + 2(\underline{\hspace{1cm}}$ cm$)$

Step 2 Use the formula for the lateral area of a pyramid. The slant height is 8 cm.

$= \underline{\hspace{1cm}}$ cm $+ \underline{\hspace{1cm}}$ cm

$= \underline{\hspace{1cm}}$ cm

Step 3 Multiply the lateral area by 2 to find the surface area of the composite figure.

Solution The surface area of the composite figure is $\underline{\hspace{1cm}}$ cm^2.

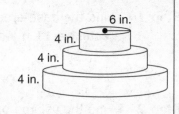

Problem 3 A baker is making a tiered cake with three layers. The radius of the top layer is 6 in. Each additional layer has a radius 4 in. longer than the layer above it. The height of each layer is 4 in. What is the volume of the cake? Round your answer to the nearest whole number.

Step 1 Find the volume of the top layer. The top layer has a radius of 6 in. and a height of 4 in.

Step 2 The radius of the middle layer is 4 in. longer than the radius of the top layer, so the radius of the middle layer is 10 in. Find the volume of the middle layer.

Step 3 The radius of the bottom layer is 4 in. longer than the radius of the middle layer, so the radius of the bottom layer is 14 in. Find the volume of the bottom layer.

Step 4 Now add the volumes of the three layers.

Solution The volume of the cake is about $\underline{\hspace{1cm}}$ cubic inches.

SHORT ANSWER QUESTIONS

Solve each problem. Round to the nearest hundredth.

1.
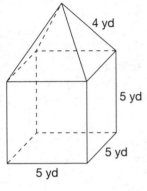
4 yd
5 yd
5 yd
5 yd
5 yd

SA = _____

2.
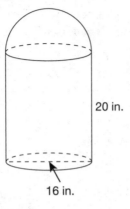
20 in.
16 in.

V = _____

3.
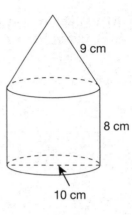
9 cm
8 cm
10 cm

SA = _____

4.
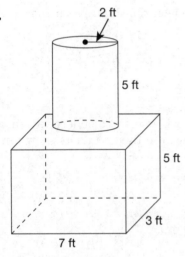
2 ft
5 ft
5 ft
3 ft
7 ft

SA = _____

5.
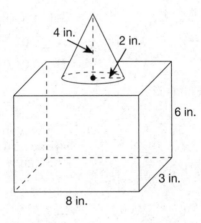
4 in.
2 in.
6 in.
3 in.
8 in.

V = _____

6.
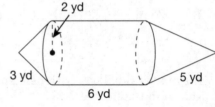
2 yd
3 yd
6 yd
5 yd

SA = _____

7. Mitzi is building a snowman. The radii of the 3 spheres of the snowman are 12 in., 8 in., and 4 in. Find the volume of the snowman to the nearest hundredth. V = _____

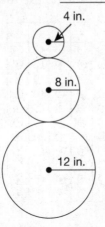
4 in.
8 in.
12 in.

8. Find the volume of the remaining region when the cone is removed from the cylinder. Leave π in your answer. Express your answer in simplified radical form.

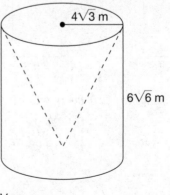
$4\sqrt{3}$ m
$6\sqrt{6}$ m

V = _____

★ STAAR PRACTICE

DIRECTIONS Read each question. Then circle the letter for the correct answer. If a correct answer is <u>not here</u>, circle the letter for "Not Here."

1 A toy building block is shown in the figure.

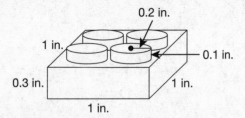

What is the surface area of the building bock?

A 0.13 in.^{2} **C** 3.45 in.^{2}

B 3.20 in.^{2} **D** 3.70 in.^{2}

2 A cylindrical balloon with hemispherical ends is shown in the figure.

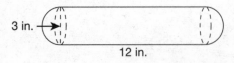

What is the volume of the balloon?

A 452 in.^{3} **C** 43 in.^{3}

B 99 in.^{3} **D** 36 in.^{3}

3 The faces of rectangular kitchen cabinets are shown in the figure.

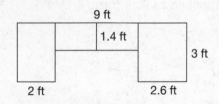

If the cabinets are 2 ft deep, what is the volume?

A 54 ft^3 **C** 27 ft^3

B 39.92 ft^3 **D** 19.96 ft^3

4 A stoplight casing consisting of a rectangular prism base and three light disks is shown in the figure.

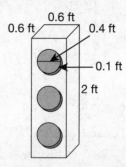

What is the volume of the stoplight casing?

A 0.01 ft^3 **C** 0.72 ft^3

B 0.04 ft^3 **D** 0.76 ft^3

5 A city water tower is made of a sphere with a cylindrical extension in the middle as shown in the figure.

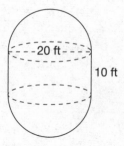

What is the surface area of the water tower? Round to the nearest hundredth.

Record your answer in the boxes below. Then fill in the bubbles. Be sure to use the correct place value.

🔶 **STAAR PRACTICE: CUMULATIVE**

· ·

DIRECTIONS Read each question. Then circle the letter for the correct answer.
If a correct answer is <u>not here</u>, circle the letter for "Not Here."

6   The lines in the figure appear to be parallel.

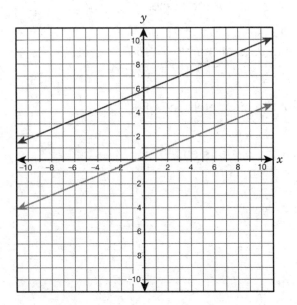

Which can be used to prove the lines
are parallel?

A   Show that the slopes of the lines are equal.

B   Show that the slopes of the lines are
negative reciprocals.

C   Show that the y-intercepts of the lines
are equal.

D   Show that the y-intercepts of the lines are
negative reciprocals.

7   The graph of triangle ABC is shown below.

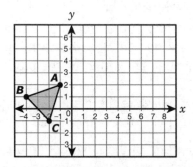

If triangle ABC is reflected across the line $x = 1$,
what is the coordinate of point B'?

A $(-4, 1)$ **C** $(6, 1)$

B $(4, -1)$ **D** $(5, 1)$

8   A right cone is intersected by a plane at an
angle perpendicular to the base and passing
through the vertex. Which figure could describe
the intersection?

A   Trapezoid   **C**   Parabola

B   Triangle   **D**   Line

9   Look at the figure below.

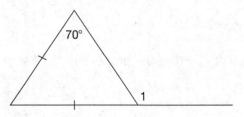

Find the measure of $\angle 1$.

A $45°$ **C** $110°$

B $70°$ **D** $125°$

Lesson 25   Circles, Sectors, and Arc Lengths

A **circle** is the set of all points in a plane that are a given distance from a point called the **center** of the circle.

A **central angle** is an angle whose vertex is the center of the circle.

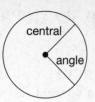

A **sector of a circle** is a region that is bounded by a central angle of a circle and its intercepted arc. The shaded area of the circle at right is a sector of the circle.

The ratio of the area A of a sector to the area of the circle is equal to the ratio of the degree measure of the intercepted arc $x°$ to the measure of the circle $360°$. This can be written as the proportion $\frac{A}{\pi r^2} = \frac{x°}{360°}$.

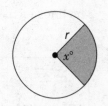

Arc length is the distance along an arc. It is a fraction of the circumference of the circle so it is measured in linear units.

The ratio of the length of an arc l to the circumference of the circle is equal to the ratio of the arc measure $x°$ to $360°$. This can be written as the proportion $\frac{l}{2\pi r} = \frac{x°}{360°}$.

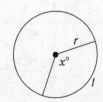

🐃 GUIDED PRACTICE

Problem 1 Find the area of sector ACB. Round your answer to the nearest hundredth.

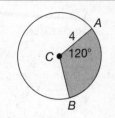

Step 1   Use the proportion $\frac{A}{\pi r^2} = \frac{x°}{360°}$. Substitute 4 in. for r and 120 for x.

$$\frac{A}{\pi r^2} = \frac{x°}{360°}$$

$$\frac{A}{\pi(4 \text{ in.})^2} = \frac{120°}{360°}$$

Step 2   Solve the proportion for A to find the area of the sector.

$$\frac{A}{\pi(4 \text{ in.})^2} = \frac{120°}{360°}$$

$$A \cdot 360° = 120° \cdot \pi(4 \text{ in.})^2$$

$$A = 120° \cdot \frac{16\pi \text{ in.}^2}{360°}$$

$$A \approx 16.76 \text{ in.}^2$$

Solution   The area of sector ACB is about 16.76 square inches.

ADDITIONAL PROBLEMS

Problem 2 Find the length of $\widehat{XY}$. Round your answer to the nearest hundredth.

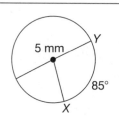

Step 1 Find the radius of the circle. Divide the diameter by 2 to find the radius.

$$r = \frac{5 \text{ mm}}{2} = 2.5 \text{ mm}$$

Step 2 Use the proportion $\frac{l}{2\pi r} = \frac{x°}{360°}$. Substitute 2.5 mm for r and 85 for x. Solve the proportion for l to find the arc length.

$$\frac{l}{2\pi(2.5 \text{ mm})} = \frac{85°}{360°}$$

$$l \cdot \underline{\hspace{2cm}} = \underline{\hspace{2cm}} \cdot 2\pi(2.5 \text{ mm})$$

$$l = \underline{\hspace{2cm}} \cdot \frac{2\pi(2.5 \text{ mm})}{\boxed{}}$$

$$l \approx \underline{\hspace{2cm}} \text{ mm}$$

Solution The length of $\widehat{XY}$ is about \underline{\hspace{2cm}} mm.

Problem 3 Find the area of the shaded region. Round your answer to the nearest hundredth.

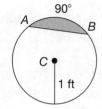

Step 1 Draw the central angle whose sides intersect the endpoints of $\overline{AB}$. The measure of $\widehat{AB}$ is 90°, so the measure of central angle ACB is also 90°. The area of the shaded region is the area of sector ACB – the area of triangle ABC.

Step 2 Find the area of sector ACB. \underline{\hspace{2cm}}

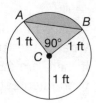

Step 3 Triangle ABC is a 45°-45°-90° triangle with height 1 ft and base 1 ft. Find the area of the triangle. \underline{\hspace{2cm}}

Step 4 Subtract the area of triangle ABC from the area of sector ACB.

Solution The area of the shaded region is about \underline{\hspace{2cm}} ft^2.

SHORT ANSWER QUESTIONS

Find the arc length (*AL*) and sector area (*SA*) to the nearest hundredth.

1. radius = 6 cm
central angle = 30°

AL = _____

SA = _____

2. radius = 8 in.
central angle = 45°

AL = _____

SA = _____

3. radius = 20 m
central angle = 120°

AL = _____

SA = _____

4. diameter = 1 inch
central angle = 100°

AL = _____

SA = _____

5. diameter = $6\sqrt{3}$ cm
central angle = 140°

AL = _____

SA = _____

6. radius = $5\sqrt{6}$ yd
central angle = 175°

AL = _____

SA = _____

7. Bob ordered a pepperoni pizza. When it arrived, each slice created a 30° angle. If the radius of each slice was 6 inches and Bob ate 5 slices, what is the area of the pizza he ate? Round your answer to the nearest hundredth. _____

8. Find the area of the shaded region. Round your answer to the nearest hundredth.

_____

9. In a circle with a radius of 10 inches, the sector area is 20π square inches. Find the arc length. Leave π in your answer. _____

10. In a circle, the measure of the arc is 120° and the arc length is 16π feet. Find the length of the radius. _____

11. Find the area of the shaded region bounded by the triangle and the sector when the radius is 12 inches and the central angle is 90°. Round to the nearest hundredth. _____

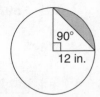

12. In a circle with radius of 7.5 cm, the arc length is 7π. Find the sector area. Leave π in your answer. _____

13. Find the area of the shaded region bounded by the triangle and the sector when the central angle is 120° and the radius is 2 feet. Leave π and a simplified radical in your answer.

_____

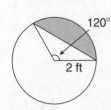

14. The spokes of a bicycle wheel create a 20° angle with the center. Each spoke is 12 inches long.
   a. What is the length of one section of the wheel? Round to the nearest hundredth. _____
   b. If there are 18 sections to the wheel, what is the circumference of the wheel to the nearest hundredth? _____

15. Find the area of the shaded region. Leave π in your answer. A = _____

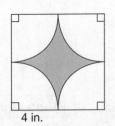

STAAR PRACTICE

DIRECTIONS Read each question. Then circle the letter for the correct answer. If a correct answer is <u>not here</u>, circle the letter for "Not Here."

1 A circle with radius 6 ft is shown in the figure below. The measure of the central angle AOB is 30 degrees.

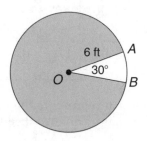

Find the area of the shaded region.

A 3π ft^2 **C** 36π ft^2

B 33π ft^2 **D** 39π ft^2

2 A circle with radius 2 cm is shown in the figure below. The measure of the central angle AOB is 60 degrees.

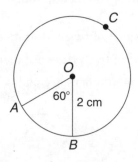

Find the length of arc ACB.

A $\frac{2}{3}\pi$ cm   **C** 2π cm

B $\frac{10}{3}\pi$ cm   **D** 4π cm

3 The area of the shaded sector of the circle in the figure is 27π ft^2 and the radius is 9 ft.

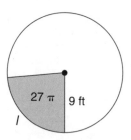

Find the measure of arc length l.

A 6π ft   **C** 18π ft

B 9π ft   **D** 27π ft

4 If the radius of a circle is doubled while the central angle remains the same, the arc length —

A doubles   **C** increases by two

B quadruples   **D** does not change

5 The length of arc m is 2π mm and the central angle is 90 degrees as shown in the figure.

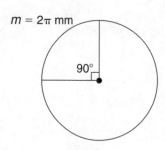

Find the area of the sector.

A 4 mm^2 **C** 16 mm^2

B 4π mm^2 **D** 16π mm^2

⭐ STAAR PRACTICE: CUMULATIVE

DIRECTIONS Read each question. Then circle the letter for the correct answer.
If a correct answer is <u>not here</u>, circle the letter for "Not Here."

6 Which expression represents the area of a triangle with a height, h, that is twice as long as the base?

A h^2

B $2h^2$

C $\frac{1}{2}h^2$

D $\frac{1}{4}h^2$

7 Lines r and s are parallel.

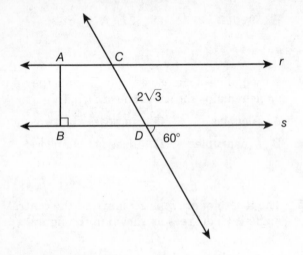

Find the length of AB.

A $2\sqrt{3}$

B $4\sqrt{3}$

C $\sqrt{3}$

D 3

8 The table below shows the relationship between the measure of an inscribed angle of a circle and the measure of its subtended arc.

Measure of Inscribed Angle	30°	40°	50°	60°	$n°$
Measure of Subtended Arc	60°	80°	100°	120°	?

Which expression represents the measure of a subtended arc cut by an inscribed angle $n°$?

A $2n$

B $\frac{1}{2}n$

C $n - 2$

D $2 - n$

9 Which of the following is true?

A The sum of three odd numbers is divisible by three.

B The product of two odd numbers is odd.

C The sum of two prime numbers is prime.

D All prime numbers are odd.

Lesson 26   Tangents, Secants, and Chords

There are three types of lines that can intersect a circle.

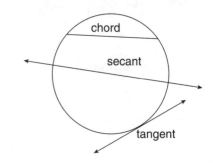

- A **chord** is a segment with endpoints that lie on a circle. A diameter of a circle is a chord.

- A **secant** is a line that intersects a circle in two points.

- A **tangent** is a line that lies in the same plane as a circle and intersects the circle in exactly one point called the **point of tangency**.

Here are some theorems about lines and circles.

1. If two chords intersect in a circle, then the product of the lengths of the segments that make up one chord is equal to the product of the segments that make up the other chord. You will prove this theorem in Problem 1.

2. If two secants share an endpoint outside a circle, then the product of the lengths of one secant segment and its external segment equals the product of the lengths of the other secant segment and its external segment.

3. If a secant and a tangent share an endpoint outside a circle, then the product of the lengths of the secant segment and its external segment equals the square of the length of the tangent segment.

GUIDED PRACTICE

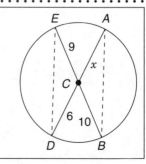

Problem 1

Prove the following theorem. Then use the theorem to find x.
Given: Circle C with chords $\overline{AD}$ and $\overline{BE}$
Prove: $AC \cdot CD = BC \cdot CE$

Step 1   Prove the theorem. Use a two-column proof.

Statements	Reasons
Circle C with chords $\overline{AD}$ and $\overline{BE}$.	Given
$\angle A \cong \angle E$, $\angle B \cong \angle D$	Inscribed $\angle$'s that intercept the same arc are $\cong$.
$\triangle ACB \sim \triangle ECD$	AA Similarity
$\dfrac{AC}{CE} = \dfrac{BC}{CD}$	Definition of similar triangles
$AC \cdot CD = BC \cdot CE$	Cross products property

Step 2   By the theorem, $AC \cdot CD = BC \cdot CE$. Substitute the values you know and solve for x.

$$AC \cdot CD = BC \cdot CE$$
$$x \cdot 6 = 10 \cdot 9$$
$$6x = 90$$
$$x = 15$$

Solution   The length of x is 15.

ADDITIONAL PROBLEMS

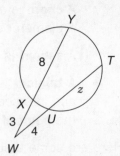

Problem 2 | Find the value of *z*.

Step 1 Find *WY* and *WT*.

$WY = WX + XY = 3 + 8 = 11$

$WT = WU + UT = 4 + z$

Step 2 Substitute the values you know and solve for *z*.

$$WY \bullet WX = WT \bullet WU$$

$$11 \bullet 3 = (4 + z) \bullet 4$$

$$33 = 16 + 4z$$

$$17 = 4z$$

$$z = \frac{17}{4} \text{ or } 4.25$$

Solution | The value of *z* is 4.25.

Problem 3 | $\overline{AD}$ is tangent to the circle. Find the value of *x* and the length of $\overline{AC}$. Round to the nearest hundredth.

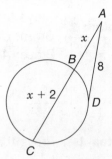

Step 1 Find *AC* in terms of *x*.

$AC = AB + BC = x + (x + 2) = 2x + 2$

Step 2 Substitute the values you know into the equation $AD^2 = AB \bullet AC$ and solve for *x*. _____

Step 3 You know from Step 1 that $AC = 2x + 2$. Substitute the value of *x* to determine *AC*.

Solution | The value of *x* is about _____.

The length of *AC* is about _____.

Measuring Up® to the Geometry End-of-Course Exam

SHORT ANSWER QUESTIONS

Solve each problem. Round to the nearest hundredth, if needed.

1.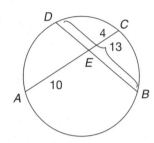

DE = _____ EB = _____

2.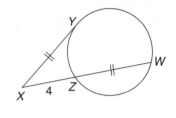

XY = _____

3.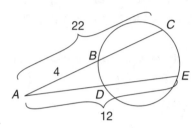

AD = _____

4.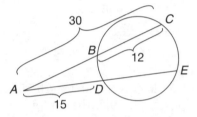

AE = _____

5.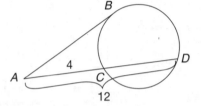

AB = _____

6.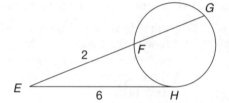

EG = _____

7.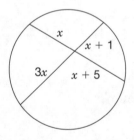

x = _____

8.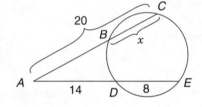

AB = _____ BC = _____

9.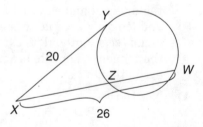

XZ = _____

10. Find the missing segment lengths. Leave your answer in simplified radical form.

AE = _____ AB = _____

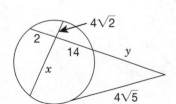

11. Find x and y. Leave your answer in simplified radical form.

x = _____ y = _____

🤠 STAAR PRACTICE

DIRECTIONS Read each question. Then circle the letter for the correct answer.
If a correct answer is <u>not here</u>, circle the letter for "Not Here."

1 A circle with two tangents and a secant intersect at a point outside the circle.

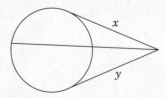

What might you conclude about the length of two intersecting tangents, x and y?

A Since both lengths are equal to the square root of the product of the lengths of the secant segment and its external segment, the tangent segments are equal to each other.

B Since both lengths are equal to the square of the external secant segments, the tangent segments are equal to each other.

C Since length x is equal to the product of the internal and external secant segments and length y is equal to the product of the secant segment and its external segment, the tangent segments are not equal to each other.

D Not Here

2 A circle with intersecting chords is shown in the figure.

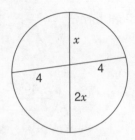

Find the length of x.

A $2\sqrt{2}$ **C** $\sqrt{2}$

B 8   **D** Not Here

3 Look at the figure.

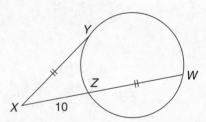

Find the length of XY.

A 8.09   **C** 65.45

B 16.18   **D** 261.8

4 The diameter of circle O is 8. The length of OB is 2. Segment AC passes through the center.

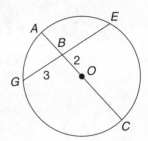

Find the length of segment EB.

A 2   **C** 4

B 3   **D** Not Here

5 Look at the figure.

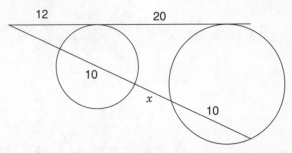

Find the distance, x, between the two circles.

A 8   **C** 32

B 9.4   **D** 64

STAAR PRACTICE: CUMULATIVE

DIRECTIONS Read each question. Then circle the letter for the correct answer. If a correct answer is <u>not here</u>, circle the letter for "Not Here."

6 Which two intersections would produce the same shape?

A The intersection of a cone and a plane parallel to its base, and the intersection of a sphere and a plane.

B The intersection of a square pyramid and a plane perpendicular to its base, and the intersection of a square prism and a plane perpendicular to its base.

C The intersection of a cylinder and a plane perpendicular to its base, and the intersection of a cylinder and a plane parallel to its base.

D Not Here

7 Which of the following would be a possible use for geometry?

A Finding the number of people who like a new product

B Finding the amount of electricity used in a light bulb

C Finding the price of a new car

D Finding the slope of a ski hill

8 If the diagonals of a parallelogram are perpendicular and congruent, what must always be true?

A The parallelogram is a kite.

B The parallelogram is a square.

C The parallelogram is a rhombus.

D The parallelogram is a rectangle.

9 Which equation is an equation of a line perpendicular to the line $y = 4$?

A $x = 2$

B $y = -4$

C $y = 4x + 2$

D $y = -\frac{1}{4}x + 2$

Lesson 27   Applications of Geometry

Geometry can be used to solve real-world problems involving probability.

Probability that uses ratios of geometric measures is called **geometric probability**.
You can use length, area, and angle measures to find geometric probability.

Length Probability Ratio

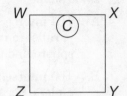

If a point is chosen at random on $\overline{AD}$, then the probability
that the point lies on $\overline{BC}$ is $\frac{BC}{AD}$.

Area Probability Ratio

If a point is chosen at random in square $WXYZ$, then the probability that
the point is in circle C is $\frac{\text{area of circle } C}{\text{area of square } WXYZ}$.

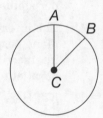

Angle Measure Probability Ratio

If a point is chosen at random in circle C, then the probability that the point
is in sector ACB is $\frac{\text{measure of sector } ACB}{360°}$.

GUIDED PRACTICE

Problem 1

A cable weather station gives the local weather report every 10 minutes beginning at
8 minutes after the hour. The local report lasts for 2 minutes. What is the probability a
local weather report will be on when you randomly turn on your television?

Step 1   Draw a line segment that is 10 units long. Show
8 minutes representing non-local programming and
2 minutes representing the local weather report.

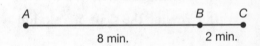

Step 2   Use the length probability ratio to find the probability.

$P(\text{local weather report}) = \frac{2}{10} = 0.2$ or 20%

Solution   The probability the local weather report will be on when you randomly turn on
the television is 20%.

🔷 ADDITIONAL PROBLEMS

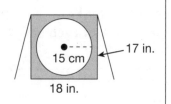

Problem 2

Simon is making a bean bag game. The goal is to toss a bean bag through the hole. Simon would like the player to have between a 30% and 35% probability of getting the bean bag through the hole if the player hits the frame. Will the design at right meet Simon's specifications?

Step 1   The rectangular frame is measured in inches and the radius of the hole is measured in centimeters. Convert 15 cm to inches so the measurements have the same units. Use the conversion factor 1 in. ≈ 2.54 cm.

Step 2   Calculate the area of the rectangular frame and the area of the hole.

Area of hole: Area of frame:

$A = \pi r^2$ $A = bh$

   $= \pi(\underline{\hspace{1cm}}$ in.$)^2$ $= (\underline{\hspace{1cm}}$ in.$)(\underline{\hspace{1cm}}$ in.$)$

   $\approx \underline{\hspace{1cm}}$ in.^{2} $= \underline{\hspace{1cm}}$ in.^{2}

Step 3   Use the area probability ratio to find the probability. $P = \dfrac{\boxed{}}{\boxed{}}$ in.^{2}

$P(\text{hitting the hole when the bag is tossed}) = \dfrac{\text{area of hole}}{\text{area of frame}}$

   $= \underline{\hspace{1cm}}$ %

Solution   The design does/does not \underline{\hspace{2cm}} meet Simon's specifications because the probability is/is not \underline{\hspace{2cm}} between 30% and 35%.

Problem 3

Darla is on a game show. She gets to spin the wheel one time and receives the amount of money the wheel lands on. What is the probability Darla wins $250?

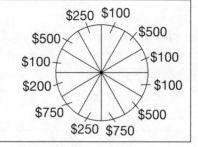

Step 1   The wheel is made up of 12 equal sectors. Determine the angle measure of each sector. 360° ÷ 12 = 30°

Step 2   Count the number of times $250 appears on the wheel. Then multiply that number by 30°. \underline{\hspace{2cm}}

Step 3   Calculate the probability using the angle measure probability ratio.

Solution   The probability of Darla winning $250 is about \underline{\hspace{2cm}}%.

SHORT ANSWER QUESTIONS

Solve each problem. Write each probability as a fraction and as a percent to the nearest whole percent. Use the diagrams for Problems 1–3.

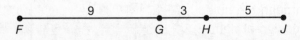
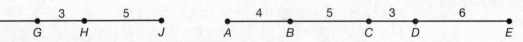

1. Find the probability that a point lies on segment *GH*.

_____ _____

2. Find the probability that a point is not on segment *FG*.

_____ _____

3. Find the probability that a point lies on segment *BC* or *DE*.

_____ _____

Use the diagram for Problems 4 and 5. For Problems 4–7, express your answer as a fraction and a percent.

4. Find the probability that a point lies in green.

_____ _____

5. Find the probability that a point does not land in blue.

_____ _____

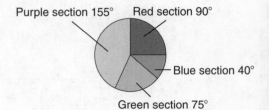

6. A cab comes to the airport every 20 minutes to pick up fares and waits for 7 minutes. Find the probability that the cab will be at the airport when you are ready to leave.

_____ _____

7. After turning on your computer, you leave to run an errand. The monitor stays on for 15 minutes, the screen saver runs for 20 minutes, and then the computer goes to sleep for 30 minutes. Find the probability that the computer will be asleep when you return from the store. Assume you will return

when your computer is still in one of these three stages. _____ ; _____

8. Which has the better probability: a) the probability that a dart will land in the triangle or b) a dart will land in the regular hexagon? Why?

_____

_____

_____

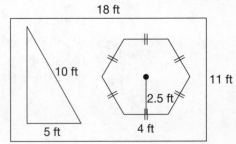

Use the diagram for Problems 9–10.

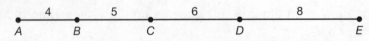

9. To create a probability of 26%, which segment would a point need to lie on?

_____

10. If the probability is 52%, which segments could the point lie on?

_____

🌵 STAAR PRACTICE

DIRECTIONS Read each question. Then circle the letter for the correct answer. If a correct answer is <u>not here</u>, circle the letter for "Not Here."

1 The figure below shows a dart-board with a diameter of 16 cm.

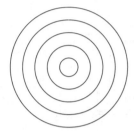

If the board's manufacturer wants players to have a 25% probability of hitting the middle circle, what should the radius of the circle be?

A 8 cm   **C** 4 cm

B 5 cm   **D** 2 cm

2 The figure below represents the probability of event A occurring in a given time period B.

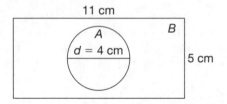

What is the probability of event A not occurring?

A 93%   **C** 23%

B 77%   **D** 7%

3 Line segment A represents the possibility of an event occurring in a certain amount of time represented by line segment B.

$A = 12$ $B = 72$

What is the probability of event A occurring?

A 86%   **C** 17%

B 83%   **D** 14%

4 The figure below is a geometric representation of the probability of different events occurring.

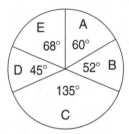

What is the probability that either Event A or Event B will occur?

A 2.4%   **C** 16.7%

B 14.4%   **D** 31.1%

5 Each of the circles in the figure below represents the chance of an event occurring.

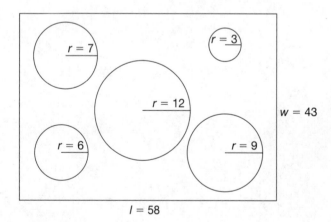

What is the probability that none of the events will occur?

A 23%   **C** 60%

B 40%   **D** 82%

★ STAAR PRACTICE: CUMULATIVE

DIRECTIONS Read each question. Then circle the letter for the correct answer. If a correct answer is <u>not here</u>, circle the letter for "Not Here."

6 Which of the following equations describes a line that is parallel to $y = 3x + 9$?

A $18x = 6y - 21$

B $3y = x + 1$

C $9x = 27y + 18$

D $3y = 3x - 27$

7 Which of the following geometric figures will be formed by a horizontal intersection of a plane with a cone?

A Ellipse

B Square

C Rhombus

D Circle

8 The figure below shows the net of a three-dimensional object.

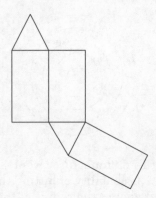

Which of the following is formed by this net?

A Square pyramid

B Cylinder

C Triangular prism

D Triangular pyramid

9 Approximately how many cubic feet of space are enclosed in a box measuring 3 meters × 3 meters × 4 meters?

A 118.1 ft^3

B 387.5 ft^3

C 1271.3 ft^3

D $3,796,170 \text{ ft}^3$

A tile pattern consists of square tiles and octagon tiles with an apothem of 3 inches and radius of 3.25 inches.

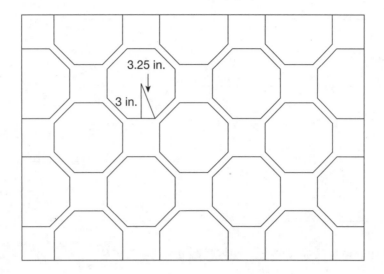

Part A   What is the area of one octagonal tile? Show your work.

Part B   What is the total area of the tiled rectangle? Show your work.

Part C   When laying tile, grout is used between each tile to seal the area between tiles.
What is the linear amount of grout, in inches, needed to surround the tiles?
(Note: Grout will not be used along the perimeter of the outer rectangle.)
Show your work.

Part D   A bottle of grout covers 300 linear centimeters. How many bottles will you need
to buy in order to grout the rectangular area? Explain your answer.

An artist creates the block letter Z as shown in the figure.

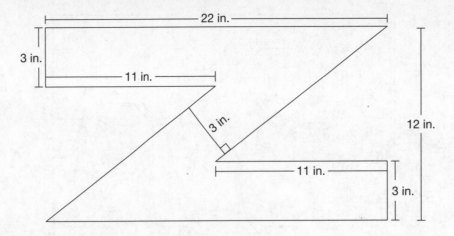

Part A   What is the area of the artist's letter? Show your work.

Part B   The artist will paint the top surface of the letter with two coats of paint. If one container of paint covers 125 square inches, how many containers of paint will the artist need to buy?

Part C   What is the perimeter of the artist's letter? Show your work. Round to the nearest tenth.

Part D   If the artist makes the letter out of 2-inch thick boards, what will be the volume of the letter? Show your work.

Two polygons are **similar** if they have the same shape but not necessarily the same size.

Two polygons are similar if and only if their corresponding angles are congruent and the lengths of their corresponding sides are proportional.

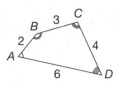

The ratio of the lengths of the corresponding sides is called the **similarity ratio** or **scale factor**.

In the figure at right, *ABCD* ~ *EFGH*. The order of the vertices identifies the corresponding parts of the figures.

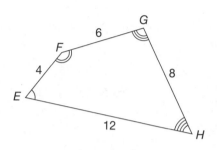

Corresponding angles are congruent:

$\angle A \cong \angle E$; $\angle B \cong \angle F$; $\angle C \cong \angle G$; $\angle D \cong \angle H$

Corresponding side lengths are proportional:

$\frac{AB}{EF} = \frac{BC}{FG} = \frac{CD}{GH} = \frac{DA}{HE} = \frac{1}{2}$

The scale factor is $\frac{1}{2}$.

★ GUIDED PRACTICE

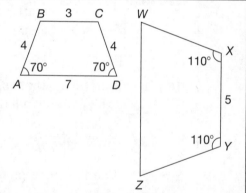

Problem 1

Trapezoid *ABCD* ~ Trapezoid *WXYZ*. Find the measure of angle *W* and the length of $\overline{YZ}$.

Step 1   The trapezoids are similar. By the similarity statement ***ABCD*** ~***WXYZ***, angle ***A*** corresponds to angle ***W***. The measure of angle *A* is 70°, so the measure of angle *W* is 70°.

Step 2   Determine the scale factor. $\overline{BC}$ corresponds to $\overline{XY}$, so the scale factor is $\frac{BC}{XY}$ or $\frac{3}{5}$.

Step 3   Use the scale factor to write and solve a proportion.

$\frac{3}{5} = \frac{4}{YZ}$

$3 \cdot YZ = 4 \cdot 5$

$3 \cdot YZ = 20$

$YZ \approx 6.67$

Solution   The measure of angle W is 70°. The length of $\overline{YZ}$ is about 6.67.

⭐ **ADDITIONAL PROBLEMS**

Problem 2

In rectangle *ABCD*, *AB* = 12 and *BC* = 7. In rectangle *LMNP*, *LM* = 20 and *MN* = 12. Determine whether *ABCD* is similar to *LMNP*.

Step 1   The figures are both rectangles so all corresponding angles are congruent.

Step 2   Write a proportion comparing the side lengths.

$$\frac{7}{12} = \frac{12}{20}$$

Step 3   Find the cross products. If they are equal, then the figures are similar.

Solution   *ABCD* is/is not _____ similar to *LMNP*.

Problem 3

Triangle *ABC* ~ triangle *DEF* with scale factor $\frac{x}{y}$. Show that the perimeters of the triangles are proportional to their scale factor.

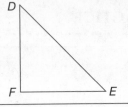

Step 1   Determine what you know. The triangles are similar so their corresponding side lengths are proportional.

$$\frac{AB}{DE} = \frac{BC}{EF} = \frac{CA}{FD} = \frac{x}{y}$$

Step 2   Use the cross products property.

$$\frac{AB}{DE} = \frac{x}{y}, \text{ so} \qquad AB = DE\left(\frac{x}{y}\right)$$

$$\frac{BC}{EF} = \frac{x}{y}, \text{ so} \qquad BC = EF\left(\frac{x}{y}\right)$$

$$\frac{CA}{FD} = \frac{x}{y}, \text{ so} \qquad CA = FD\left(\frac{x}{y}\right)$$

Step 3   The perimeter of triangle *ABC* is *AB* + *BC* + *CA*. By substitution:

$$AB + BC + CA = DE\left(\frac{x}{y}\right) + EF\left(\frac{x}{y}\right) + FD\left(\frac{x}{y}\right)$$
$$= \left(\frac{x}{y}\right)(DE + EF + FD)$$

Step 4   Write the ratios of the perimeters:

$$\left(\frac{x}{y}\right)\frac{(DE + EF + FD)}{(DE + EF + FD)} = \frac{x}{y}$$

Solution   The perimeters of the triangles are proportional to their scale factor, $\frac{x}{y}$.

SHORT ANSWER QUESTIONS

Solve each problem. Round to the nearest hundredth.

1.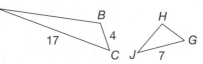

△ABC ~ △GHJ

GJ = _____

2.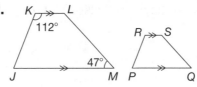

□ JKLM ~ □ PRSQ

m∠S = _____

3.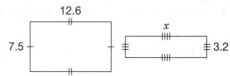

x = _____

4.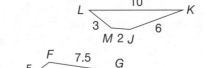

Is EFGH ~ JMLK? _____

5.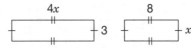

x = _____

6. True or False? A rhombus and a kite are similar.

_____

7. △PQR ~ △XYZ

PQ = 5x + 4, XY = 8,

QR = 7x − 4, YZ = 10

x = _____

8. △ABC ~ △STV

AB = x, AC = 4,

ST = 6, SV = x + 5

x = _____

9. △ABC ~ △DEF

∠A = 3x + 2y, ∠C = 36

∠D = 2x + 8y, ∠F = x + 3y

x = _____ y = _____

10. ABCD ~ MNPQ; List all of the corresponding sides that are proportional and the corresponding angles that are congruent.

_____

11. The similarity ratio of a hot wheels car to a model car is $\frac{1\ inch}{13\ inches}$. If the model car has a length of 45 inches, how long is the hot wheels car to the nearest hundredth? L = _____

12. Name three shapes that will always be similar to each other. _____

_____

13. Bob has a blueprint drawing of a painting for his house. On the blueprint, the length of the painting is 11.2 inches and the width is 5.6 inches. Bob knows that the length of the actual painting is 15 feet. How wide is his painting? W = _____

14. Jen is standing between two trees and creates two similar triangles with the tops of the trees. She is 6 feet away from a tree that is 32 feet tall and 2.5 feet away from the other tree. How tall is the second tree? Round to the nearest hundredth.

H = _____

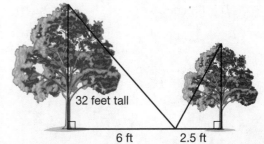

STAAR PRACTICE

DIRECTIONS Read each question. Then circle the letter for the correct answer. If a correct answer is <u>not here</u>, circle the letter for "Not Here."

1 The two polygons shown are similar.

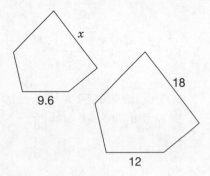

What is the value of *x*?

A 6.4

B 14.4

C 15.6

D 22.5

2 Kiara drew a pattern of similar triangles, as shown in the figure.

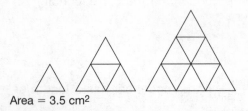

Area = 3.5 cm²

She will continue the pattern by drawing a fourth figure of a similar triangle with four small triangles across the bottom. What will be the area of the fourth figure in this pattern?

A 42 cm²

B 49 cm²

C 56 cm²

D 63 cm²

3 The figure shows two similar polygons.

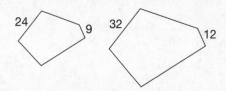

What is the scale factor for the polygons?

A $\frac{4}{3}$ **C** $\frac{5}{3}$

B $\frac{3}{2}$ **D** $\frac{5}{4}$

4 *ABCD ~ EFGH*. The scale factor is 3:4.

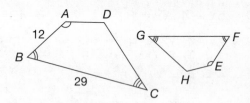

What is the side length of $\overline{EF}$?

A 6   **C** 9

B 7   **D** Not Here

5 The figure shows two similar polygons.

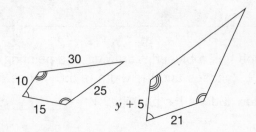

What is the value of *y*?

A 6   **C** 8

B 7   **D** 9

STAAR PRACTICE: CUMULATIVE

DIRECTIONS Read each question. Then circle the letter for the correct answer.
If a correct answer is <u>not here</u>, circle the letter for "Not Here."

6 The figure below is an equilateral triangle. Use what you know about special right triangles and the formula for finding the area of a triangle to derive the formula for finding the area of an equilateral triangle.

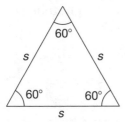

Which formula can be used to find the area of an equilateral triangle?

A $A = s^2 \frac{\sqrt{2}}{4}$

B $A = s^2 \frac{\sqrt{3}}{4}$

C $A = s \frac{\sqrt{3}}{4}$

D $A = s^2 \frac{\sqrt{2}}{2}$

7 The figure below is an octagonal prism. Use what you know about faces (F), vertices (V), and edges (E) of three dimensional shapes to develop a conjecture about Euler's Formula.

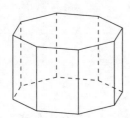

Which formula below is Euler's Formula?

A $V - E + F = 2$

B $V + E + F = 2$

C $V - E - F = 2$

D $V + E - F = 2$

8 The outline of a circular playground with a diameter of 3 meters is shown below.

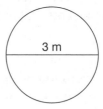

What is the approximate volume of woodchips required to cover the playground 1.5 inches deep?

A 10.6 in.^{3}

B 42.41 in.^{3}

C 16,434.5 in.^{3}

D 65,738 in.^{3}

9 How long is the third side of a right triangle that has a hypotenuse with a length of 17 and a side with a length of 8?

A 19

B 17

C 15

D 12

Two triangles are similar if and only if their corresponding angles are congruent and their corresponding side lengths are proportional. There are several ways to prove triangles similar:

1. **AA Similarity Postulate (Angle-Angle)**: If two angles of one triangle are congruent to two angles of another triangle, then the triangles are similar.

2. **SAS Similarity Theorem (Side-Angle-Side)**: If an angle of one triangle is congruent to the corresponding angle of another triangle and the sides that include this angle are proportional, then the two triangles are similar.

3. **SSS Similarity Theorem (Side-Side-Side)**: If the corresponding side lengths of two triangles are proportional, then the triangles are similar.

By AA Similarity, every right triangle with a given acute angle is similar to every other right triangle with the same acute angle measures. The ratio of two sides of a right triangle is called a **trigonometric ratio**.

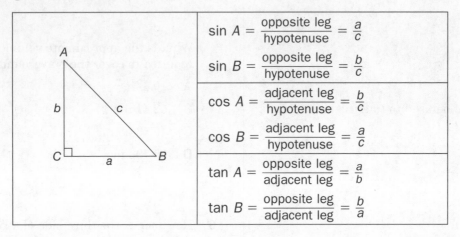

$$\sin A = \frac{\text{opposite leg}}{\text{hypotenuse}} = \frac{a}{c}$$

$$\sin B = \frac{\text{opposite leg}}{\text{hypotenuse}} = \frac{b}{c}$$

$$\cos A = \frac{\text{adjacent leg}}{\text{hypotenuse}} = \frac{b}{c}$$

$$\cos B = \frac{\text{adjacent leg}}{\text{hypotenuse}} = \frac{a}{c}$$

$$\tan A = \frac{\text{opposite leg}}{\text{adjacent leg}} = \frac{a}{b}$$

$$\tan B = \frac{\text{opposite leg}}{\text{adjacent leg}} = \frac{b}{a}$$

GUIDED PRACTICE

Problem 1 Determine whether $\triangle AED \sim \triangle ABC$.

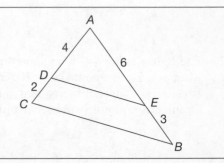

Step 1   Both triangles include $\angle A$. By the reflexive property, $\angle A \cong \angle A$.

Step 2   Determine whether the two pairs of corresponding sides adjacent to $\angle A$ are proportional.

$$\frac{AD}{AC} = \frac{4}{4 + 2} = \frac{4}{6} = \frac{2}{3}$$

$$\frac{AE}{AB} = \frac{6}{6 + 3} = \frac{6}{9} = \frac{2}{3}$$

Solution   By the SAS similarity theorem, $\triangle AED \sim \triangle ABC$.

★ ADDITIONAL PROBLEMS

Problem 2 Find each of the following trigonometric ratios:
sin *D*, cos *D*, tan *D*, sin *E*, cos *E*, tan *E* .

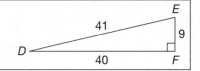

Step 1 Use the table of trigonometric ratios.

Step 2 Write each ratio.

$\sin D = \dfrac{9}{\square}$ $\qquad$ $\cos D = \dfrac{\square}{41}$ $\qquad$ $\tan D = \dfrac{\square}{40}$

$\sin E = \dfrac{\square}{\square}$ $\qquad$ $\cos E = \dfrac{\square}{\square}$ $\qquad$ $\tan E = \dfrac{\square}{\square}$

Solution

$\sin D = \dfrac{\square}{\square}$, $\cos D = \dfrac{\square}{\square}$, $\tan D = \dfrac{\square}{\square}$,

$\sin E = \dfrac{\square}{\square}$, $\cos E = \dfrac{\square}{\square}$, $\tan E = \dfrac{\square}{\square}$.

Problem 3 The courtyard of a museum is shaped like a right triangle. What is the perimeter of the courtyard? Round to the nearest hundredth.

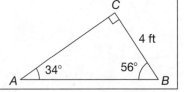

Step 1 Write and solve an equation to find $\overline{AB}$.

$\sin 34° = \dfrac{4 \text{ ft}}{AB}$

$AB = \dfrac{4 \text{ ft}}{\sin 34°}$

$AB \approx 7.15 \text{ ft}$

Step 2 Write and solve an equation to find $\overline{AC}$. You can also use the Pythagorean Theorem to find $\overline{AC}$.

$\tan 56° = \dfrac{\square}{\square}$

$\underline{\hspace{1.5cm}} = \underline{\hspace{3cm}}$

$AC \approx \underline{\hspace{2cm}} \text{ ft}$

Step 3 Add the side lengths to find the perimeter.

Solution The perimeter is about \underline{\hspace{2cm}} ft.

SHORT ANSWER QUESTIONS

Solve. Write AA, SAS, or SSS to prove the triangles are similar. Round to the nearest hundredth.

1.

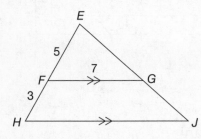

△EFG ~ △EJH by _____

HJ = _____

2.

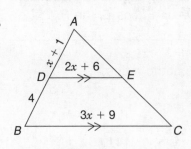

△ADE ~ △ABC by _____

x = _____

3.

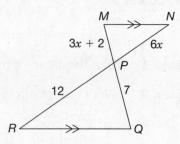

△MPN ~ △QPR by _____

x = _____

Solve using trigonometric ratios. Round to the nearest hundredth.

4.

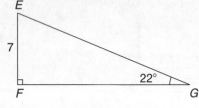

EG = _____

5.

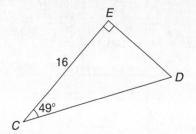

ED = _____

6.

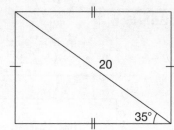

Area = _____

Perimeter = _____

Solve each problem. Round to the nearest hundredth.

7. Given △GHJ ~ △MPN, ∠G = 26°, ∠M = (2x − 3y)°, ∠H = (4x + 2y)°, ∠P = 84°;

x = _____ ; y = _____

8. x = _____ ; y = _____ ;

Perimeter = _____ ; Area = _____

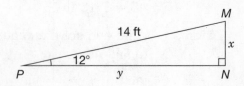

9. The Fullers want to carpet their living room which is in the shape of a right triangle. They know one angle is 42 degrees. The length of the living room is 20 ft. What is the width of the room to the nearest foot? W = _____ What is the area of the living room to the nearest square foot? A = _____

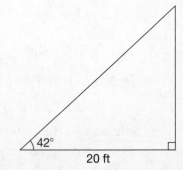

★ STAAR PRACTICE

DIRECTIONS Read each question. Then circle the letter for the correct answer.
If a correct answer is <u>not here</u>, circle the letter for "Not Here."

1 Angle B and angle E are congruent in the figure.

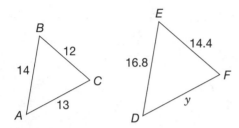

What value of y will make the triangles similar?

A 15.6   **C** 11.9

B 13.4   **D** 10.8

2 Look at the two triangles in the figure.

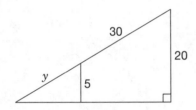

What value of y will make the triangles similar?

A 1   **C** 5

B 4   **D** 10

3 The figure shows two similar triangles.

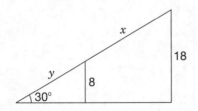

What is the value of x?

A 16   **C** 20

B 18   **D** 22

4 Look at the two triangles in the figure.

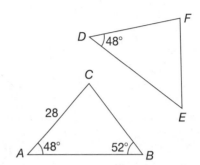

Which of the following would prove
that the two triangles are similar?

A Angle F must equal 52°.

B Angle E must equal 52°.

C Side DF must equal 28.

D Side EF must equal 28.

5 Look at the triangle.

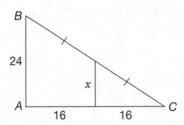

What is the value of x?

A 10

B 12

C 14

D 16

★ STAAR PRACTICE: CUMULATIVE

DIRECTIONS Read each question. Then circle the letter for the correct answer. If a correct answer is <u>not here</u>, circle the letter for "Not Here."

6 In the figure below, $\triangle X'Y'Z'$ is a dilation of $\triangle XYZ$.

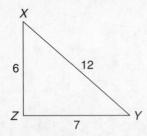 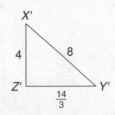

What is the scale factor?

A $\frac{14}{3}$

B $\frac{3}{4}$

C $\frac{2}{3}$

D $\frac{1}{3}$

7 A right triangle has one side equal to 4.2 cm and a hypotenuse 6.3 cm. What is the length of the other side?

A 4.7 cm

B 5.2 cm

C 6.4 cm

D Not Here

8 What is the volume of a right cone that has a radius of 2.4 cm and height 6.3 cm?

A 24 cm³

B 32 cm³

C 38 cm³

D 44 cm³

9 Which of the following could be the lengths of the sides of a right triangle?

A 1, 1, 2

B 5, 7, 9

C 9, 12, 15

D 10, 12, 14

     Measuring Up® to the Geometry End-of-Course Exam

Recall that **similar polygons** have proportional corresponding sides.

If two polygons are similar with a scale factor $\frac{x}{y}$, then

- corresponding perimeters have a ratio of $\frac{x}{y}$

- corresponding areas have a ratio of $\frac{x^2}{y^2}$

Similar solids have corresponding linear measurements in proportion.

If two solids are similar with a scale factor $\frac{x}{y}$, then

- corresponding areas have a ratio of $\frac{x^2}{y^2}$

- corresponding volumes have a ratio of $\frac{x^3}{y^3}$

 GUIDED PRACTICE

Problem 1

If you double the linear dimensions of the prism at right, you create a prism that is similar to the original. What is the effect on the volume of the prism? Answer the question by finding the volumes of the similar prisms. Then use what you know about the dimensions of similar solids to check your work.

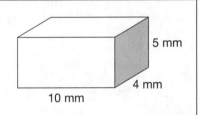

5 mm
4 mm
10 mm

Step 1   Double the linear dimensions of the prism to determine the dimensions of the similar prism.

Step 2   Find the volume of each prism.

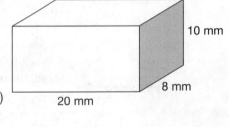

10 mm
8 mm
20 mm

Volume of smaller prism:

$V = Bh$

$= (10 \text{ mm})(4 \text{ mm})(5 \text{ mm})$

$= 200 \text{ mm}^3$

Volume of larger prism:

$V = Bh$

$= (20 \text{ mm})(8 \text{ mm})(10 \text{ mm})$

$= 1600 \text{ mm}^3$

Step 3   Now compare the volumes. $200(8) = 1600$. The volume of the larger prism is 2^3 or 8 times greater.

Step 4   Check your work. The scale factor is $\frac{2}{1}$, so the corresponding volumes have a ratio of $\frac{2^3}{1^3}$ or 8. This means the volume of the larger prism is 8 times the volume of the smaller. The answer checks.

Solution   The volume of the larger prism is 8 times the volume of the original prism.

★ ADDITIONAL PROBLEMS

Problem 2

This year, Sela designed the rectangular herb garden shown at right. Next year, she would like to have an herb garden that is 1.5 times as long and 1.5 times as wide as this year's garden. What will be the perimeter and area of next year's garden?

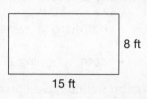

8 ft

15 ft

Step 1 Find the perimeter and area of this year's garden.

$P = 2l + 2w = 2(\underline{\hspace{1cm}} \text{ ft}) + 2(\underline{\hspace{1cm}}) \text{ ft} = \underline{\hspace{1cm}}$

$A = bh = (\underline{\hspace{1cm}} \text{ ft})(\underline{\hspace{1cm}} \text{ ft}) = \underline{\hspace{1cm}} \text{ ft}^2$

Step 2 Determine the scale factor. The two gardens have a scale factor $\frac{1}{1.5}$.

Step 3 The perimeters have a ratio of $\frac{1}{1.5}$. Write and solve a proportion to find the perimeter of next year's garden.

$\frac{1}{1.5} = \frac{46}{x}$ \underline{\hspace{2cm}}

Step 4 The areas have a ratio of $\frac{1^2}{1.5^2} = \frac{1}{2.25}$. Write and solve a proportion to find the area of next year's garden.

$\frac{1}{2.25} = \frac{120}{x}$ \underline{\hspace{2cm}}

Solution

The perimeter of next year's garden will be \underline{\hspace{1.5cm}} ft.

The area of next year's garden will be \underline{\hspace{1.5cm}} ft^2.

Problem 3

A soup manufacturer wants to decrease the size of his can by $\frac{1}{3}$ to reduce production costs. How much less material will be needed per can if the current can has a radius of 1.8 in. and a height of 4.5 in.? Round to the nearest hundredth.

Step 1 Find the surface area of the current can. The formula for the surface area of a cylinder is $SA = L + 2B$ or $SA = 2\pi rh + 2\pi r^2$. \underline{\hspace{2cm}}

Step 2 The scale factor is $\frac{1}{3}$, so the corresponding surface area has a ratio of $\frac{1^2}{3^2}$ or $\frac{1}{9}$.

Step 3 Divide the surface area of the current can by 9 to find the surface area of the new can. \underline{\hspace{1.5cm}}

Step 4 Subtract to find the difference in areas.

Solution

The new can needs about \underline{\hspace{2cm}} square inches less material than the current can.

SHORT ANSWER QUESTIONS

For each of the figures below, calculate by what factor the given value will change if the linear dimensions are doubled. Check your answer by calculating the new area or perimeter of the figure. Round your answers to the nearest hundredth.

1.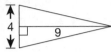

Scale Factor = _____ P_2 = _____

2.

Scale Factor = _____ A_2 = _____

3.

Scale Factor = _____ C_2 = _____

4.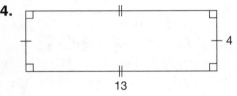

Scale Factor = _____ A_2 = _____

5.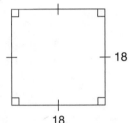

Scale Factor = _____ P_2 = _____

6.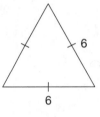

Scale Factor = _____ A_2 = _____

For each of the figures below, calculate by what factor the given value will change if the linear dimensions are all halved. Check your answer by calculating the new surface area or volume of the figure. Round your answers to the nearest hundredth.

7.

Scale Factor = ___ SA_2 = _____

8.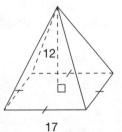

Scale Factor = ___ V_2 = _____

9.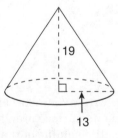

Scale Factor = ___ V_2 = _____

10. Marco has two rubber balls. The diameter of the first ball is one-third the diameter of the second ball. The volume of the second ball is 381.7 cm^3. What is the volume of the first ball to the nearest hundredth? _____

11. The Great Pyramid of Giza is approximately 147 m high and 230 m wide. Shannon constructs a scale model of the pyramid with a height of 29.4 cm. What is the ratio of the surface area of Shannon's model compared to the surface area of the Great Pyramid of Giza?

_____

STAAR PRACTICE

DIRECTIONS Read each question. Then circle the letter for the correct answer. If a correct answer is <u>not here</u>, circle the letter for "Not Here."

1 The ratio relating the surface area of two similar solids is $\frac{x}{y}$. Which of the following ratios represents the relationship between the volumes of the two solids?

A $\dfrac{x^{\frac{1}{2}}}{y^{\frac{1}{2}}}$

B $\dfrac{x}{y}$

C $\dfrac{x^2}{y^2}$

D $\dfrac{x^{\frac{3}{2}}}{y^{\frac{3}{2}}}$

2 Anne has a family photo measuring 12 cm by 16 cm. By how much will the area of the photo increase if the length of each side is increased by a factor of 1.5?

A 432 cm^2

B 240 cm^2

C 192 cm^2

D 2.25 cm^2

3 A cylinder with a diameter of 2 cm and a height of 8 cm has its surface area doubled. By what factor does the volume of the cylinder change?

A 3

B $2\sqrt{2}$

C 2

D $\sqrt{2}$

4 The radius of a sphere is increased to 300% of its original value. By what factor does the volume of the sphere increase?

A 27

B 9

C 3

D 2

5 A square pyramid with a volume of 224 cm^3 has its linear dimensions divided by two. What is the volume of the new, smaller pyramid?

A 112 cm^3

B 56 cm^3

C 28 cm^3

D 8 cm^3

6 The Moon's diameter is $\frac{1}{4}$ the diameter of Earth. What fraction expresses the ratio of the Moon's volume to the volume of Earth?

A $\dfrac{1}{64}$

B $\dfrac{1}{8}$

C $\dfrac{1}{4}$

D $\dfrac{1}{2}$

 Measuring Up® to the Geometry End-of-Course Exam

STAAR PRACTICE: CUMULATIVE

DIRECTIONS Read each question. Then circle the letter for the correct answer.
If a correct answer is <u>not here</u>, circle the letter for "Not Here."

7 What is the surface area of a circle with a diameter of 6 cm?

  A 36π cm^2

  B 12π cm^2

  C 9π cm^2

  D 6π cm^2

8 The equation of a line is shown below.

$$18x = 3y - 9$$

What is the slope of the line?

  A -3

  B 1

  C 3

  D 6

9 What is the height of an equilateral triangle with a side length of 8 cm?

  A 11.3 cm

  B 8.9 cm

  C 6.9 cm

  D 5.7 cm

10 What is the volume of a cylinder with a diameter of 4 cm and a height of 6 cm?

  A 24π cm^3

  B 12π cm^3

  C 6π cm^3

  D 3π cm^3

A rectangular city park is divided into three play areas: 2 right triangles and 1 quadrilateral, as shown below.

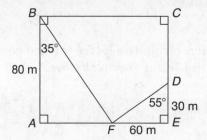

Part A   How can you prove that △ABF ~ △EFD?

Part B   What is the scale ratio of △ABF to △EFD?

Part C   What are the missing lengths of △ABF and △EFD?

Part D   What is the ratio of the corresponding areas of △ABF to △EFD? Explain.

The city is building a wheelchair ramp and needs to supply support beams for it. The highest beam is 3 feet and the horizontal length of the ramp is 16 feet.

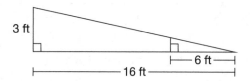

Part A   Explain why the two triangles formed by the ramp and support beams are similar.

Part B   If the first support beam is located 6 feet from the beginning of the ramp, how tall is the first support beam?

Part C   What is the scale ratio of the small triangle to the large triangle?

Part D   How long is the ramp to the nearest hundredth of a foot?

Part E   If the ramp is 4 feet wide and constructed of poured concrete around the steel support beams, what is the ratio of the corresponding volumes of the small to large triangular prisms? Explain.

Theorems, Corollaries, and Postulates

Alternate Interior Angles Theorem	If two parallel lines are cut by a transversal, then alternate interior angles are congruent.
Alternate Exterior Angles Theorem	If two parallel lines are cut by a transversal, then alternate exterior angles are congruent.
Same-Side Interior Angles Theorem	If two parallel lines are cut by a transversal, then same-side interior angles are supplementary.
Corresponding Angles Postulate	If two parallel lines are cut by a transversal, then corresponding angles are congruent.
Chords and Lines Theorem 1	If two chords intersect in a circle, then the products of the lengths of the segments that make up one chord is equal to the product of the segments that make up the other chord.
Chords and Lines Theorem 2	If two secants share an endpoint outside a circle, then the product of the lengths of one secant segment and its external segment equals the product of the lengths of the other secant segment and its external segment.
Chords and Lines Theorem 3	If a secant and a tangent share an endpoint outside a circle, then the product of the lengths of the secant segment and its external segment equals the square of the length of the tangent segment.
Pythagorean Theorem	In a right triangle, the sum of the squares of the lengths of the legs is equal to the square of the length of the hypotenuse: $a^2 + b^2 = c^2$
Converse of the Pythagorean Theorem	If $a^2 + b^2 = c^2$, then the triangle is a right triangle.
Pythagorean Inequalities theorems	If $c^2 > a^2 + b^2$, then the triangle is obtuse and if $c^2 < a^2 + b^2$, then the triangle is acute.
SSS Congruence Postulate (Side-Side-Side)	If three sides of one triangle are congruent to three sides of another triangle, then the triangles are congruent.
SAS Congruence Postulate (Side-Angle-Side)	If two sides and the included angle of one triangle are congruent to two sides and the included angle of another triangle, then the triangles are congruent.
ASA Congruence Postulate (Angle-Side-Angle)	If two angles and the included side of one triangle are congruent to two angles and the included side of another triangle, then the triangles are congruent.
AAS Congruence Theorem (Angle-Angle-Side)	If two angles and a non-included side of one triangle are congruent to two angles and the corresponding non-included side of another triangle, then the triangles are congruent.

HL Congruence Theorem (Hypotenuse-Leg)	If the hypotenuse and a leg of one right triangle are congruent to the hypotenuse and a leg of another right triangle, then the triangles are congruent.
AA Similarity Postulate (Angle-Angle)	If two angles of one triangle are congruent to two angles of another triangle, then the triangles are similar.
SAS Similarity Theorem (Side-Angle-Side)	If an angle of one triangle is congruent to the corresponding angle of another triangle and the sides that include this angle are proportional, then the two triangles are similar.
SSS Similarity Theorem (Side-Side-Side)	If the corresponding side lengths of two triangles are proportional, then the triangles are similar.
45°-45°-90° Triangle Theorem	In a 45°–45°–90° triangle, the length of the hypotenuse is $\sqrt{2}$ times the length of a leg.
30°-60°-90° Triangle Theorem	In a 30°-60°-90° triangle, the hypotenuse is twice the length of the shorter leg and the longer leg is $\sqrt{3}$ times the length of the shorter leg.
Inscribed Angles Corollary	If two inscribed angles intercept the same arc, then they are congruent.
Third Angle Theorem	If two angles in one triangle are congruent to two angles in another triangle, then the third angles are also congruent.
Linear Pair Postulate	If two angles form a linear pair, then they are supplementary. If two angles form a linear pair, then the sum of the angles is 180°.
Congruent Supplements Theorem	If two angles are supplementary to the same angle (or to congruent angles), then the angles are congruent.
Congruent Complements Theorem	If two angles are complementary to the same angle (or to congruent angles), then the angles are congruent.
Vertical Angle Theorem	Vertical angles are congruent.
Right Angle Congruence Theorem	All right angles are congruent.
Right Angle Theorem	If two angles are congruent and supplementary, then each angle is a right angle
Parallel/Perpendicular Theorem	In a plane, if two lines are perpendicular to the same line, then they are parallel.
CPCTC	Corresponding parts of congruent triangles are congruent.

Congruence Properties

Property	Segments	Angles
Reflexive	$\overline{AB} \cong \overline{AB}$	$\angle X \cong \angle X$
Symmetric	If $\overline{AB} \cong \overline{CD}$, then $\overline{CD} \cong \overline{AB}$	If $\angle X \cong \angle Y$, then $\angle Y \cong \angle X$.
Transitive	If $\overline{AB} \cong \overline{CD}$ and $\overline{CD} \cong \overline{EF}$, then $\overline{AB} \cong \overline{EF}$.	If $\angle X \cong \angle Y$ and $\angle Y \cong \angle Z$, then $\angle X \cong \angle Z$.
Substitution	If $\overline{AB} \cong \overline{CD}$ and $AB = 60$, then $CD = 60$.	If $\angle X \cong \angle Y$ and $m\angle Y = 85°$ then $m\angle X = 85°$.
Multiplication	If $4 \cdot AB = 60$, then $AB = 15$.	If $5 \cdot m\angle Y = 85°$, then $m\angle Y = 17°$.
Addition	If $AB + 4 \cdot AB = 100$, then $5 \cdot AB = 100$.	If $5 \cdot m\angle Y + m\angle Y = 100°$, then $6 \cdot m\angle Y = 100°$.

Geometry Reference Materials

CIRCUMFERENCE

Circle	$C = 2\pi r$	or	$C = \pi d$

AREA

Triangle	$A = \frac{1}{2}bh$
Rectangle or parallelogram	$A = bh$
Rhombus	$A = \frac{1}{2}d_1 d_2$
Trapezoid	$A = \frac{1}{2}(b_1 + b_2)h$
Regular polygon	$A = \frac{1}{2}aP$
Circle	$A = \pi r^2$

SURFACE AREA

	Lateral	Total
Prism	$S = Ph$	$S = Ph + 2B$
Pyramid	$S = \frac{1}{2}Pl$	$S = \frac{1}{2}Pl + B$
Cylinder	$S = 2\pi rh$	$S = 2\pi rh + 2\pi r^2$
Cone	$S = \pi rl$	$S = \pi rl + \pi r^2$
Sphere		$S = 4\pi r^2$

VOLUME

Prism or cylinder	$V = Bh$
Pyramid or cone	$V = \frac{1}{3}Bh$
Sphere	$V = \frac{4}{3}\pi r^3$

COORDINATE GEOMETRY

Midpoint	$\left(\dfrac{x_1 + x_2}{2}, \dfrac{y_1 + y_2}{2}\right)$
Distance formula	$d = \sqrt{(x_2 - x_1)^2 + (y_2 - y_1)^2}$
Slope of a line	$m = \dfrac{y_2 - y_1}{x_2 - x_1}$
Slope-intercept form of a linear equation	$y = mx + b$
Point-slope form of a linear equation	$y - y_1 = m(x - x_1)$
Standard form of a linear equation	$Ax + By = C$

RIGHT TRIANGLES

Pythagorean theorem	$a^2 + b^2 = c^2$

Trigonometric ratios

$$\sin A = \frac{\text{opposite leg}}{\text{hypotenuse}}$$

$$\cos A = \frac{\text{adjacent leg}}{\text{hypotenuse}}$$

$$\tan A = \frac{\text{opposite leg}}{\text{adjacent leg}}$$

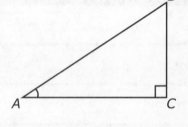

30° – 60° – 90° triangle

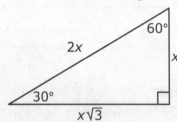

45° – 45° – 90° triangle

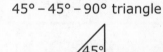

Graph Paper